A PATH TO
THE DOOR

A PATH TO THE DOOR

A CHRONICLE OF PETTERS'
INVENTIONS, BUSINESSES,
PEOPLE, ENGINES AND
AIRCRAFT, 1895–1995

Kenneth D'Maurney Gibbons

ALAN SUTTON PUBLISHING LIMITED
IN ASSOCIATION WITH
LISTER-PETTER LIMITED

First published in the United Kingdom in 1995
Alan Sutton Publishing Limited
Phoenix Mill · Far Thrupp · Stroud · Gloucestershire

British Library Cataloguing in Publication Data
A catalogue record for this book is available from the British Library

ISBN 0-7509-1006-2

Typeset in 11/13 Bembo.
Typesetting and origination by
Alan Sutton Publishing Limited.
Printed in Great Britain by
Hartnolls, Bodmin, Cornwall.

Contents

List of Illustrations

Foreword

I am delighted to have been asked to write a foreword to this profile of the rise of a pre-eminent, international diesel engineering company.

In this, Lister-Petter's centenary year, it is highly appropriate to look at past achievements. And Lister-Petter – which combines the names and industrial experience of two fine businesses – can be very proud of the long tradition of technical and design innovation it has inherited from both Listers and Petter.

Kenneth D'Maurney Gibbons has written a detailed account of the growth of Lister-Petter, of its products and of the businessmen and engineers who played a key role in the development of its diesel engines right up to the introduction of the innovative 'Alpha' range. This book will be of interest to both the layman and those of a more technical bent.

I am pleased to record that the company's success story continues to this day. As a member of the international BTR Group, it has benefited from the financial, technical and managerial strengths of one of the world's largest industrial engineering corporations. Under BTR's influence, investment and new product development have continued to be put to the fore and, as a result, Lister-Petter looks set to continue its success story as it enters its second hundred years of engine production.

Alan R. Jackson AO
Chief Executive, BTR plc

Author's Note and Acknowledgements

The writing of *A Path to the Door* is the fulfilment of a promise made thirty years ago, a promise made to myself when I completed my first short history article on the Petter family. The research carried out to prepare that article indicated a far greater and much more intriguing story to be unravelled. The following sets the scene on my involvement with the company and I hope demonstrates my proud association with it for over three decades.

I first saw Petters' factories at Staines in March 1964, when I was appointed as Assistant Public Relations Officer. The Causeway and Ironbarks works stretched three-quarters of a mile along the A30, past Staines Bridge and up the Chertsey Road. The two main works were separated from each other by Thorpe Road and the entire factory complex was backed by the electrified railway to Waterloo. The prospect of working among eleven hundred others seemed daunting, for I was accustomed to a third of that, but I was soon made to feel at ease. Wherever my duties took me in that labyrinth of workshops and offices, the family atmosphere prevailed. This was noticed by visitors, customers and suppliers alike; but then, it had always been so, as I was to discover.

I wanted to learn about the Petter family; their beginnings, their early products, and various moves and takeovers that had eventually brought them to this historic Causeway factory, once owned by Lagonda Cars Ltd. As an aid to my learning, my boss John Tennant suggested I research a short article for the *Hawker Siddeley News*, the group newspaper, to commemorate the company's seventy-fifth year.

So, I journeyed to Petters' birthplace, Yeovil, in Somerset, to explore the dusty attic of the *Western Gazette*. There, surrounded by racks of sheepskin-bound volumes of the paper, some dating back two hundred years, I traced the daily happenings of Petters in the late 1800s. Without realizing it, I had begun a lifetime's ambition. The more I read, the more fascinated I became; this was no ordinary family of ironmongers. A visit to the town museum was rewarded by the sight of the first Petter oil engine used to power their horseless carriage of 1895. The history article was duly published and for months the company received letters from some of the 96,000 readership of *Hawker Siddeley News,* for it was sent to all the group's employees, suppliers and customers. Many of the letters came from engineers who had started their careers with Petters and were now only too pleased to proclaim that honour.

Working with John Tennant was an experience. He was ex-army and a wonderful host who believed in delegation rather than involvement. Our frequent journeys together, to Petters' other factory at Hamble, form some of my favourite memories.

Having disposed of the day's post to his secretary, he would usher me in the direction of the car park. Although he could drive, his preference was motor-cycling, apparently spending much time and care on his machine. His perpetual delight was planning the annual holiday, invariably to some remote area of Europe to which he journeyed on the 'bike', and for weeks afterwards regaled the staff and visitors alike with 'joys of the open road' stories.

He would settle himself into the passenger seat of my Mini and proceed to open the day's *Times* full width, leaving me to peer round the broadsheet to see the road ahead. Occasionally, he would explode with wrath or guffaw at some newspaper story before nodding off to sleep within the first twenty miles. When the Pig and Whistle at Privett was reached, he would open his eyes and declare it was time for coffee and buttered toast. The return trip was somewhat similar except that he fell asleep without the aid of the paper and awoke at the West Meon Hut where toasted teacakes were the order of the day.

The factory complex at Staines was surrounded by residential property which reflected the growth of the area in a collection of architecture from different eras, each leaning on the other to form a random development dictated by decades of varying demands. The Causeway factory was the larger of the two main factories and still retained the low headroom of its early beginnings as the home of Lagonda Cars. This low structure gave a gloomy atmosphere to the main machine shop and assembly lines. The ancillary departments of laboratory, standards, inspection, maintenance, stores, planning, technical sales, drawing office and the despatch/shipping departments were all housed in the Causeway works. The work pattern allowed basic machining at the Thorpe Road end, progressing through sub-assembly areas and moving conveyors to finished engines ready for testing and despatch at the other end of the works some three hundred yards away.

In later years, an expensive automatic transfer line for the machining of aluminium engine crankcases was accommodated, while later still the assembly lines for the same engines were installed to run parallel with their cast-iron counterparts. The Ironbarks works were also dim and grimy from the machining of cast-iron components and, like Causeway, had the pungent smell of cutting fluid that poured in torrents from the various machine tools.

This creamy-white fluid disappeared into underfloor channels to be recirculated, its smell intermingled with that of diesel and lubricating oil from the test bays to permeate shoes and clothing alike. Ironbarks produced machined crankcases and assembled PJ engines, and was generally a much quieter place than Causeway works. Fronting Ironbarks works was a comparatively modern two-storey office block, later extended to three floors over the main entrance. The ground floor housed the personnel, commercial and buying departments while upstairs were the home sales, cost office, public relations department and telephone exchange. The third floor housed the overseas department, the boardroom, the directors' dining room and a visitors' lounge that overlooked Staines Bridge over the River Thames.

The Research and Development Centre, opened in 1961, was a purpose-designed building with a pleasing appearance dominated by a large glass entrance hall and open staircase echoing the theme of the main entrance of Ironbarks works, complete with a restored Handyman vintage engine. The ground floor with its manager's office and workshops also housed the test cells and their remote monitoring booths. The technical director's office with conference room, design office and technical liaison departments were on the first floor.

Behind the R&D Centre was a building into which few visitors ventured. The noise, smell and dirt were uninviting, for this unpleasant place contained the automatic shot-blasting conveyor on which iron castings were fettled; for every ton of lead shot used to clean the castings, a ton of waste metal was recovered. The Bridge works, situated beside the Thames on the opposite side of the road to the main factories, housed the service depot and the company garage. It was one of Petters' network of six service depots located between Hamble and Aberdeen.

Staines was an ideal commuting town for London thanks to the fast electrified railway which operated to Waterloo. Just across the river bridge was the High Street, allowing Petters' workers easy shopping access during their lunch hour. Heathrow airport was only some twenty minutes away by car, which at times was too close. I remember seeing a Boeing 707 drop an engine in the gravel pits behind the factory and make a crash landing at the airport. On another occasion, a Trident airliner crashed on takeoff, ending up just a hundred yards or so short of Staines High Street and in a direct line with the Petter factory.

However, the airport's close proximity was a boon when one was welcoming foreign visitors or arriving home from an overseas tour. In the late sixties, groups of overseas agents were invited to conferences, sometimes accompanied by their wives, who were entertained with organized visits to local places of interest. The visits included Windsor Castle, Runnymede Air Force Memorial, the site of the signing of Magna Carta, the Royal Savile Gardens and Virginia Water, while evening entertainment for all was arranged in the medieval atmosphere of Great Fosters, once a Henry VIII hunting lodge. I still have visions of overseas visitors trying their hand at longbow archery on the floodlit lawns and joining in sixteenth-century madrigals!

When John Tennant retired in 1966, he insisted the company should offer me his position as Public Relations Officer, a role I was pleased to accept. So with a staff of nine we settled down to produce sales promotion services for six product divisions, located at Staines and Hamble, while liaising corporate identity with Hawker Siddeley Group in London. I always found time to include a visit to owners of early Petter oil engines whenever they came to light. This often led to the company purchasing the vintage power units to add to their museum after Arthur Coote, the long-suffering apprentice supervisor, and his 'boys' had restored and show-finished them. Many of the vintage engines were subsequently shown on Petter exhibition stands as evidence of their durability.

In 1965, I presented a Handyman to the Science Museum and made the purchase of a 5 hp version from a family in Princes Risborough. The engine had powered equipment in the family's butchery business. However, someone forgot to drain the cooling system on a cold winter's night, resulting in a crack extending almost completely around the cylinder. The local smith had affected an excellent repair by riveting a large metal plate around the cylinder so successfully that the Handyman was still in working order when it was demonstrated to me forty years later! The engine was purchased and show-finished and placed in the museum but not before it had been proudly shown by Petters at the Royal Show, Stoneleigh.

When the museum collection at Staines exceeded twenty it was removed to Hamble, but the problem of storage persisted until 1973 when it passed to David Edgington in Wiltshire for safe-keeping. David, a stationary engine enthusiast, became founding editor of the *Stationary Engine* magazine, and is an authority on the restoration of Petter oil engines. The oldest exhibit in the company's collection was the first high-speed, single-action steam engine made by Ben Jacobs in *c.* 1893. Two other unusual exhibits were a Nautilus grate and a door from a James B. Petter bread oven. I found the oven, still thick with soot, installed in a country cottage. As the building was going to be modernized and the oven demolished, I had the doors dismantled, cleaned and sent to join the rest of the museum collection. The photographs of the door in situ in the cottage where James B. Petter and his workmen had installed it in the mid-1800s are still in my collection (see p. 6).

I became Communications and Marketing Manager in the late seventies before I left in 1983 to form my own advertising and PR agency. When Jack Regis, director and export sales manager, and David Mayne offered me the advertising and sales promotion work for the company in the following year, I was delighted to be involved again. For two exciting years, I devised and published Petter trade press adverts and wrote editions of *Engine Torque International*, a house magazine I started in the sixties. Other business interests intervened in 1985, and these required me to turn my attentions away from Petters just before their merger with Listers. However, as someone once wrote, 'despite the changes, everything remains the same', for I still find myself writing about Petters!

The 5 hp Handyman purchased by the author for Royal Show restoration in 1965. Note the blacksmith's repair along the length of the cylinder, allowing the engine to operate for a further forty years

Part of the Petter stand at the 1965 Royal Show, Stoneleigh, designed by the author for the company's 75th anniversary. It features the restored 5 hp Handyman engine (minus the blacksmith's repair)

Acknowledgements

Without sounding too much like the recipient of an award, I would like to thank all those past colleagues whose help, understanding and comradeship over the last thirty years have contributed to the writing of this book. My thanks are also due to those professional helpers who gave so willingly of their time: Carol Strachan of *The Engineer*; Robin Ansell, Reference Librarian, Somerset Library Service; Jane Campbell, NDDC Barnstaple Library; Ann Henderson, Commercial Information Librarian, Key Information (Plymouth); the Falmouth branch of the Cornwall County Library; Audrey Edgeler, Barnstaple historian; and Anne Bennett and Jonathan Falconer at Alan Sutton Publishing Ltd. My best wishes and grateful thanks to all those who worked for Petters Ltd during the period 1964 to 1979 and who gave me their support. In particular I would like to thank my secretaries, Maureen Doughty and Beryl Deevy, and assistants Eric Freeman, Robin Saunders, Ian Callendar and Tony Marter.

I am grateful to the following for specific memories and assistance. Hugh Marsden for his foresight in employing me in the first place; to John Tennant for recommending me to take his place on retirement; to Jack Regis, Arthur Carrodus and Bill Rees for being excellent bosses; to John Gale, George Owen, Roly Cawson and Bill Stratton for making my job enjoyable; to George Dibble for his forgiving attitude to my accounting; to Ron Kennedy for allowing me to buck the purchasing system and for being my excellent deputy chairman of the PSSA; to Anna Neale and Beryl Richards for getting me ahead of the MD's queue; to Esme and all her girls on the switchboard for preferential treatment; to Florence Roshier and her sister Vi for speedy settlement of my expenses; to Bob Jones for those enjoyable lessons in the use of 'spanners'; to Cedric Brown for his helpful advice on the chairmanship of the PSSA; to Frank Clarke, Geoff Perkin, Peter Attwooll, Dennis Suffield, Jack Kirkwood, Stan Pallett, Jim Layn, Tony Small, Nobby Clark, Charlie Munden, Norman Grimes, Roy Skinner and all those in sales and service.

My very sincere thanks also go to Nick Hollick for his rapid translations and wonderful knowledge of international travel; to Jack Grey and George Baker and their drivers who gave their all in delivering exhibits to me at country shows or meeting me at impossible times at Heathrow or Gatwick. To George Hancock, Trevor Hitchcock, Bill Stagg, Alec Currie and everyone at Hamble who gave friendly assistance. A big thank you to Dukes Court and all who sailed in her, including Capt. Dick Law, Bill Baird, Tony Guttridge, Brian Mee, Jock Dall, Stuart Shakespeare, Ken Gainer, Charlie Brookes, Guy Checketts, Paul Grunfeld, Hugh Edwards and all the girls, in particular my wonderful wife Gill.

Finally, I would pay tribute to Clem A'Court, Jim Ridgeway and Keith Bailey for their extreme patience and dedication during the ten years they accompanied me on photographic locations and gave so freely of their expertise. Without their professionalism much of the Petter photographic library would not have existed and I would not have been tempted to emulate their art.

Prelude

The Petter family of craftsmen settled in Barnstaple, North Devon, in the early 1800s and progressively created businesses along the High Street. By 1860, they occupied at least twelve different properties with a variety of trades. These grew until 1890, when they included cabinet and furniture makers, boot and shoe-makers, saddle and harness makers, newspaper publishers, coopers, ironmongers, blacksmiths, ironfounders, booksellers and stationers, postmaster, grocer and tea dealers, chemist and druggist, milliners, outfitters, brewers and maltsters, estate and insurance agency, architect and surveyor and timber merchants.

The first Petter tradesmen in Barnstaple were George, John, James and Henry; they probably came from London, as records note that Henry originated from there to start the Shapland & Petter business of cabinet and furniture making in 1821. George was a boot- and shoe-maker while John Sen., possibly the grand-father of the founder of Petters Ltd, formed a partnership to launch the *North Devon Journal* in 1824, a local newspaper still published today.

James, born 1796, was trained as a cooper, and started his business around 1843, eventually selling it to William Ackland in 1865. John Petter Jun., born 1821, became a brazier, tin-plate worker, smith and ironmonger and was the father of James B. Petter who years later founded the engine company in Yeovil. Edwin Petter, born 1826, was a saddler, corn merchant, seedsman, brewer and eventual owner of Petter & Son, trading as the Anchor Brewery, while Frederick Petter, born 1830, was a grocer, tea dealer and chemist. Edward Petter, *c.* 1832, was possibly a bookseller in the partnership of Hayman & Petter, leaving in 1854 to partner John Jun. in the ill-fated North Devon Iron Foundry and Agricultural Machinery works on Rolle Quay.

Frederick William Petter was an architect and surveyor in the 1890s and Charles Henry Petter established a timber merchants in the same year. However, our interest relates to John Petter Jun., who commenced his ironmongery business in 1843, adding his other trades as business expanded to eventually employ seven men and eight boys, with three of them living in, by 1861. With his younger brother Edward and £1,400 capital from his ironmongery business, he built a 200 ft x 120 ft iron foundry and workshop on Barnstaple's Rolle Quay in 1854 and commenced work as the North Devon Iron Foundry and Agricultural Machinery business.

In 1856, John Jun. decided to leave the partnership on the grounds of ill health and recruited the services of a relation, William Oatey. Oatey was a smith in Wadebridge and was needed to take over from John, as Edward was not a craftsman. The new partnership of Petter & Oatey started in 1856 with capital of £550, but within fourteen months an iron merchant from Bristol bankrupted them for £3,500. John Petter Jun. regained £860 of his original £1,400 investment, while Edward Petter and Wm Oatey received just £10 each when the property was sold to T.L. Willshire of the Barnstaple Old Foundry in 1858.

John Jun. continued his ironmongery business at Sheffield House in the High Street, where he was selling Bodley and Register stoves and grates, bar iron, lead, sheet copper, zinc, lamps, glasses, oil and wicks. He eventually closed the business in 1865 and moved his family to Yeovil. Petter Brothers of Barnstaple was formed in 1870, with possibly Edward and Henry trading as house furnishers. They added an estate agency in 1879.

PETTER PATENTS – 1881 TO 1910

Following John Petter Jun.'s move to Yeovil in 1865, he and his son James Bazeley Petter progressed as ironmongers and heating engineers.

One can see that 'necessity being the mother of invention' no doubt complemented their need to produce their own saleable merchandise. This inventive ability was passed on to successive generations of the family. Throughout the latter part of the nineteenth century and for the first decade of the twentieth, various Petter inventors filed patent applications for a variety of interesting products. James started the trend in November 1881 with his Nautilus grate and fireplace designs and followed these with a patent for insulated oven doors two years later. The grates were improved by the addition of an ash-can in 1884 and an increase in radiated heat two years later.

Together with a W.J. Waterman they produced several inventions dealing with gloves, concave metal fencing posts, stoves and fireplace draught control, smoke extraction chimneys for public buildings, underfloor air supply to fireplaces and the jointing of gas, steam and water pipes. All these patents were filed in 1887. In 1888, James designed a system for securing stove pipes to roofs and a watering can combined with a hose. By the turn of the century, he was improving flues for boilers and a system of oil/spirit lighting for buildings. An intriguing design for an oscillating trough for cheese making was filed in 1891, followed by one for a root-cutting machine.

Being surrounded by glove makers, James could not resist improving their lot, so in 1892 he designed an automatic bodkin for inserting ribbons and lace into fabrics. At the age of twenty, Ernest Petter filed his first patent for a special glove fastening. In the same year, he applied for a patent for a device to ensnare wild birds, while James turned his attentions to the dairy industry in 1895 with a design for a cheese curd cutter, and an easy-clean milk pail and cheese tub.

The next year brought Petters' first venture into internal combustion engine design with an application for the opposed positioning of the inlet and exhaust valves to assist cleaning and replacement. By 1897 James was back to Nautilus grates, with an opening canopy design and a compartment positioned beneath the kitchen stove for drying vegetable waste. Guy Petter entered a patent for cycling costumes in 1898, while Percy produced designs for a horseless carriage brake, an electric motor and a mowing/reaping machine. Guy and Ernest patented the exhaust-heated tube ignition for oil engines in 1900 to overcome the need for continuous flame heating. This brought about the rapid acceptance of oil engines and their development. Ernest started the new century with an application for an air-operated water pump for deep wells, while his father broke new ground with a design for window ventilation bars.

Harry (James H.B.) and his father (James B. Petter) continued the quest for dust- and ash-handling equipment with their designs for a dustbin and an ash sorter in 1903. Percy decided that mechanical assistance was required below stairs, so produced a boot- and shoe-cleaning/polishing machine in the same year. Ernest entered his proposals for a device that adjusted oil engine speed in 1904, while his elder brother Harry and their father turned their attentions to a machine for manufacturing building bricks.

Two applications for internal combustion engine patents in 1906 were abandoned in the same year. Harry and his father designed a manhole frame that breathed and Ernest returned to the engine scene in 1907 with the famous SP piston ring. The SP ring was bored eccentrically to assist in obtaining uniform pressure on cylinder walls. In 1907, Ernest assisted his father with an application for baffle plates in fireplaces and boilers, and by 1909 Ernest had developed his variable speed control for oil engines. The application for patent for the speed control was accompanied by an application covering a warming device for fuel oil; no doubt with an eye on the Russian market and their winters. Percy concluded the race for patent applications prior to the establishment of Petters Ltd with his 1910 design of oil engine fuel injection, though this application was later abandoned.

CHAPTER ONE

1852–97

A Family Affair

Gifted inventors were prolific in the late nineteenth century but the trait seldom extended to successive generations of the same family. The Petter family was a notable exception. Their name became synonymous with the invention of stoves, ovens, fire-grates, oil engines, motor cars, tractors, aircraft, pianos, razors, fencing and a multitude of agricultural and dairy equipment. Petter oil engines became the hallmark of quality, reliability and durability for industrial, agricultural and marine applications from the end of the nineteenth century for the next hundred years.

This inventive family created industrial and aviation companies, the products of which influenced the way of life and indeed, after one hundred years, the very government of the nation. It has often been said that the Petter story began when James Bazeley Petter, an ironmonger in Yeovil, invented an oil engine for a horseless carriage he had decided to make. This was one of the first British cars in this country, designed in 1895. So why did an industrious but struggling nineteenth-century ironmonger risk his family fortune in the design and manufacture of motor cars? Why, after initial success with their 'horseless carriage', did they fail to rank among the famous car makers of the day? Perhaps the answers to these questions are to be found in their background, for we know from the early history noted in the Preface, that the family were talented but varied in the extreme. Certainly, John Petter, born in 1821 to become a brazier, tin-plate worker, smith and ironmonger in Barnstaple, was the guiding influence. With his younger brother Edward, he established the North Devon Iron Foundry and Agricultural Machinery business on Rolle Quay. By the age of thirty, he had established a small business empire, making the most of the great mechanization of agriculture through his manufacturing and retail facilities.

As business grew, John Petter became a respected member of the community and was appointed a local councillor. However, he found this role difficult for he

James Bazeley Petter, *c.* 1895, son of
John Petter Jun. and founder of James
B. Petter & Sons

could not tolerate the complacency sometimes practised by fellow aldermen and
became known for his outspoken views, to the annoyance of others.

In 1854 a fellow councillor refused to sit on the same committee, and there
followed considerable adverse comment in the local press, leading to a confrontation
between John Petter and a reporter from the *North Devon Journal*. This was made all
the more embarrassing for the Petter family had founded the paper in 1824 with
John Avery. The meeting became heated, leading to the councillor being accused of
using abusive language. It would appear this unfortunate incident, followed by the
bankruptcy of the North Devon Foundry run by Edward Petter and William Oatey,
concluded a period of dissatisfaction with the Barnstaple area, and John Petter
decided to sell his businesses to seek similar interests elsewhere. In August 1865, he
and his wife Eliza, née Bazeley from Hayle, Cornwall, together with their eighteen-
year-old son, James Bazeley Petter and daughters Eliza and Helen, moved 75 miles
to Yeovil, Somerset. John was an astute businessman as well as being an excellent
craftsman, for he realized the importance of the London, South Western and Great
Western railways that were being junctioned at Yeovil.

The Romans had viewed the Axminster, Dorchester and Bath trader tracks with similar satisfaction, leading them to build a settlement close to the intersection of those important paths of communication near what is now Yeovil. Some eighteen hundred years later it was discovered that the eastern edge of Petters' Westland Aircraft airfield, built by the company in 1917, was on the site of part of the Roman settlement. When the villa with its two sections of tessellated pavements was excavated, a quantity of twelve hundred coins dating from AD 300–400 also came to light, and these were deposited in the South Somerset Museum in Yeovil.

In 1865 the population of Yeovil were mostly employed in glovemaking, or the treatment and manufacture of sheepskin and leather goods, while the rolling hills surrounding the town provided thriving horticultural and agricultural industries. This wealth of industry led to the establishment of two busy markets, a fact that did not go unnoticed by John Petter, who saw this expanding environment as a place to regain his skills as an ironmonger and engineer.

Shortly after arriving in the town he purchased the long-established ironmongery business of Josiah Hanham at 15 High Street, a business that is still trading today under the name Hill & Sawtell, although the Petter family interest in the business ceased in the late 1950s shortly before Percy Petter's death.

James Bazeley Petter became manager of the shop and three years later, when he married Charlotte Waddams Branscombe, they were given the business as a wedding present. Charlotte was the daughter of Henry Waddams, a rubber merchant in Bristol, and Elizabeth Branscombe.

The ironmongery business with its engineering workshop continued to operate under John's name for some time before changing to James B. Petter. It was no ordinary retail ironmongers for they employed eleven men and four boys to carry out the work of bell-hanging, plumbing, gas-fitting, tin-plate working, smithing and hot-water engineering. Their speciality was the sale and installation of hot-air stoves for horticultural buildings, churches and halls.

The shop sold iron and brass bedsteads, kitchen ranges and stoves, boilers, lamps, baths, cutlery, razors, knives, cash and jewel boxes, lawn mowers, rollers, garden engines and seats, brushes of all types and kitchen utensils. By 1872 the business had progressed well enough for James, aged twenty-five, to purchase the Yeovil Foundry in Clarence Street, in the Huish area of the town. This was a well-established iron and brass foundry dating back some two hundred years.

James and Charlotte lived over the shop premises with their three male shop assistants and two domestic servants. Charlotte was a member of the Exclusive Brethren and attended church several times each Sunday, while James sometimes managed to escape to his beloved garden and workshop.

Having acquired the foundry, James made the existing manager, Henry J.

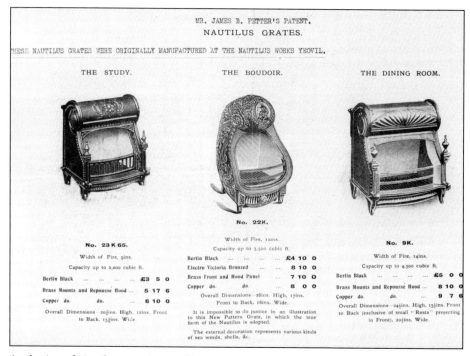

A selection of Nautilus grates invented by James B. Petter in 1881 and manufactured in the grate works at Yeovil, *c.* 1881–1901

Edgar, a 36-year-old Dorset man, a partner. They commenced trading as Petter and Edgar with the objective of producing a range of agricultural implements from their own castings, in much the same way as John Petter had done in North Devon. During the intervening years the agricultural machine trade had grown, so there was good reason to stock proprietary spare parts for the leading makes of machinery in use. The Yeovil Foundry became one of the first major stockists of spare parts.

James Bazeley Petter was an innovative engineer, with perhaps his most famous invention being the range of Nautilus grates in 1881. The grates were made of decorative cast iron in the Petter foundry and were an extremely efficient method of heating large rooms.

The Nautilus grates soon became fashionable among the leading families throughout Britain; Queen Victoria had them installed in Osborne House, her favourite home on the Isle of Wight, and also at Balmoral. The range of styles was increased, leading to the need for more workers in the Nautilus Grate works that had been built in 1881 at the end of John Petter's garden on Hendford Hill.

A Nautilus grate purchased
by the author for Petters'
product museum in 1969

Among the new staff and apprentices taken on was Herbert Swetman, who
stayed with Petters for forty-seven years, during which time his son also joined
the company. Later, Herbert's grandson Percy Swetman also joined Petters and
was still with them in 1964 when the company was located at Staines,
Middlesex. That kind of family loyalty stayed with Petters throughout their long
history, combining with the products to produce an enviable reputation.

In the next ten years, James applied for seventeen patents, most of them for
Nautilus grates. Other patent applications included: fireplaces; insulated oven
doors; fencing posts from metal sections; anti-fire chimneys for theatres and
public buildings; gas, steam and water pipe joints; oil and spirit lighting; bodkins
for fabrics; an oscillating cheese trough and a root-cutting machine. The Yeovil
Foundry was located on an area of land that later became Seaton's Garage, and
in 1993 was redeveloped as a Tesco supermarket car park.

James and Charlotte had fifteen children. Twelve survived childhood and
predictably, the first, born in 1871, was named after his father, although the
initials H.B. were added. James H.B. was always referred to as Harry. Guy B.

Petters' ironmongery shop in Yeovil High Street, *c.* 1900

Petter was born in 1872 with the identical twins, Ernest and Percy, a quarter of an hour apart, on 26 May 1873. Hugh W. arrived in 1874 and Mary, the first of the daughters, was born in 1875. The following year, Gertrude was born. John followed in 1879, Claude A. in 1881, Richard C. in 1883 and two more daughters, Eliza and Evelyn B., in 1886 and 1890.

As the family grew in size, they moved from above the High Street shop to The Grange, a large detached house situated in The Park area of Yeovil. To help Charlotte with the family a nanny, nurse, governess, cook and housemaid were employed.

When John Petter retired in about 1887, then a JP and founder of the Constitutional Club in Yeovil, he moved from his Hendford Hill house to The Grange. However, financial constraints caused James and his family to move from The Grange to above new premises acquired at 20 High Street. Ernest and Percy had been sent to Mount Radford boarding school in Exeter, but shortly before their sixteenth birthday, in 1889, the worsening financial situation caused their education to be abandoned and they returned home to start work.

Ernest and Percy joined their elder brother James H.B. and younger brother Hugh as apprentices in their father's business. Guy continued his studies at the Royal College of Science. The sixteen-year-old apprentices commenced a five-

A Petter bread oven, *c.* 1883, found by the author in 1970 and purchased for the company's museum

year training programme that took them through most of their father's business interests. In common with the other apprentices they were paid 2*s* a week, rising to 10*s* by the end of their training. The work was long and hard but varied because of the many aspects of James B. Petter's business. Relaxation led to an interest in model aircraft and the work of John Stringfellow at nearby Chard. Stringfellow died in 1883 and his flying models had passed to his dentist son F.J. Stringfellow, who continued the development work in a minor way. Percy made the journey to Chard to witness some of the test flights and also make models of his own, but family events soon put a stop to any further Petter experimental work with model aircraft. Henry J. Edgar, James's partner in the foundry, died in a road accident involving a horse-drawn trap, and a new manager was appointed, only to resign just as the twins were finishing their apprenticeship. James considered 21-year-old Percy competent to take charge of the foundry in Clarence Street, and the engineering works in Vicarage Street, and this he did with the help of Guy. James continued to supervise the ironmongery and heating business with Harry and Hugh. Percy's lack of experience caused several costly mistakes which led to a fully experienced

Ben Jacobs, Petters' first
designer and maker of their
1893 steam engine and
1895 oil engine

foreman being appointed for the foundry and engineering works. The
businesses were now trading as James B. Petter & Sons and being run on a loose
partnership basis with James in total financial control and often refusing any
suggestions for change. The new foreman was Ben Jacobs, from Sibleys of
Martock, one of the largest engineering works in southern England, who made
farm equipment and a small oil engine used to drive some of their products.
Ben Jacobs was an all-round engineer, draughtsman, pattern-maker and
machinist; one of his first tasks at Petters was to design and make a single-acting,
high-speed steam engine.

In 1894 the *Boy's Own Paper* carried a series of articles entitled 'How to Make
a Model Gas Engine'; at that time, many publications carried stories of
combustion engine development and the latest achievements of 'horseless
carriages' in Europe.

Percy's own history of the company, written in 1933, when he was sixty years
of age, alleges that Jacobs was approached with the idea that Petters should make
an engine with the objective of installing it in a suitable cart as an experimental

An early Petter trademark based on Percy Petter's signature and the basis of the modern script and diamond insignia

'horseless carriage'. Apparently, the new foreman suggested they could design a better one, and together with Percy and Guy, the twins' elder brother, they did just that.

The engine was built and installed in a 'horseless carriage' in 1895 and used extensively on the roads around Yeovil and Montacute, even giving rides at local fêtes. Popular belief has suggested that after being unsuccessful in a prized motoring competition, the idea of cars was abandoned and the experience used to produce the first Petter stationary engines for agricultural use. Research shows this is a simplified version of what actually happened.

James, the father, was still very much in control of the purse strings and agreed to form the Yeovil Motor Car & Cycle Co., but decided that the newly created engine should be developed for stationary use on farm equipment, products that the firm were well-established in marketing. One and two horse-power versions were developed and shown at the Somerset County Show in 1896.

A publication in 1895, believed to be the *Boy's Own Paper*, stated that Petters were experimenting with an autocar and that successful trials had taken place. A subsequent edition published a letter from Percy thanking them for mentioning Petters' experiments. He confirmed, 'The principle of the engine is precisely similar to that of the fixed oil engines we are making, but it is mounted on a light steel frame instead of the heavy cast-iron bed, and has a steel water jacket in place of cast-iron'. In conjunction with Hill and Boll, a local firm of

A Petter patent petroleum oil engine of 1896

coachbuilders, the first car was built. Percy's letter to the magazine also stated, 'As you will see, the car makes no pretence to elegance of design, as it was merely an adaptation for experimental purposes, but Messrs H & B who are well known makers of high-class carriages, have in hand some very elegant designs, for which we are preparing motors'.

Percy continued, 'The short notice in your issue of the 14th inst., has given us a large number of enquiries and it will be as well if you will kindly mention in further noticing the car that we are not as yet open to book orders for quick delivery, and it will probably be well into the summer [1896] before we shall be able to offer autocars for sale'. That date tallies with the first appearance of Petter engines at the Somerset show, where the second one built was sold to a Mr Tudway of Wells for his dairy. The very first one was sold to a Mr Jeanes of Dorset prior to the show.

For the automotive engine they removed the heavy, cast-iron bed-plate and large-diameter flywheel from a 1 hp stationary engine, replacing them with parallel steel bars and a smaller, lighter flywheel. Otherwise, the engine in the

Petters' first automotive oil engine of 1895

autocar was the same, with a 3.5 in bore and a 6 in stroke and a gross weight of 120 lb. Lubrication was provided by means of a hollow crankshaft containing sufficient oil for a day's run. The vehicle used a two-seat, phaeton carriage weighing 1,008 lb and had a top speed of 10 mph with a two–speed gearbox.

Several years later, the engine was presented to the Yeovil Museum as an example of the company's early engineering achievements. On 3 April 1896, *The Engineer* published a review of the first Petter horseless carriage with an illustration of a Petter 1 hp agricultural oil engine and made reference to it as an existing range of products.

On 1 May 1896, James B. Petter applied for patent of a design relating to the position and extraction of inlet and exhaust valves on oil engines. This enabled both inlet and exhaust valves to be removed for cleaning through the inlet port. By the end of the year, Petters were showing their stationary engines in London at the Royal Smithfield Show, followed in July 1897 by 1 hp, 2.5 hp and 5 hp models at the Royal Show. It would have been impossible for the company to have exhibited those products if they had not already existed prior to the Crystal

The Petter horseless carriage of 1895 with James B. Petter, legs crossed, James H.B. Petter and in the rear, left to right, Ernest and Percy Petter

Palace motor competition as has been suggested, because the motor competition took place on 31 May and the Royal Show was held during the first week of July 1897. Another popular misconception is that Petters produced their first horseless carriage for the 1897 motor competition.

In fact, the 1895 car was powered by a single-cylinder, 1 hp engine while the competition car of 1897 entered by the Yeovil Motor Car & Cycle Co., owned by Petters, was powered by a twin-cylinder, 3 hp engine. Between 1895 and 1897 the company produced twelve cars.

The movement of 'horseless carriages' on the roads of Britain was controlled by the Locomotive Act of 1865, which required all vehicles to be preceded by a pedestrian walking at 4 mph holding a red flag. Later, in 1878, the requirement for the red flag and the pedestrian was removed and finally, in 1896, the speed was raised to 14 mph. Petters used one of their apprentices, Theo Stagg, for the task of carrying the red flag. In 1961, his son Bill became manager of the Petter Transport Refrigeration division based at Hamble, Southampton, another example of long-term family loyalty within the company.

Relaxation of the Locomotive Act was celebrated by fifty-four motorists taking part in a drive from London's Hyde Park to Brighton, an event perpetuated by the Veteran Car Club with a similar outing every November.

CHAPTER TWO

1897

The Crystal Palace Competition

The Engineer magazine announced its intention to promote a 'horseless carriage' competition with prize money of 1,100 guineas in 1896. Petters saw this event as an opportunity to publicize their car, gain possible further orders and recoup some of the money spent on developing their stationary and automotive engines. This was also the culmination of two years' hard work involving the manufacture of at least twelve different vehicles. The event was to have been held in October 1896, but was postponed until the spring of 1897 as the organizers felt that motor car inventors needed more time, as several were experimenting with new designs and prototypes.

The magazine's explanation for staging the competition is interesting. They considered the public required vehicles with speed, durability, comfort and safety.

The average horseless carriage cost nearly £300, and while *The Engineer* expressed the view that tests in France indicated that light oil engines could be used for locomotion, Britain had produced nothing likely to meet the demands of the public. Apparently, a lot of criticism was aimed at current legislation and the way it affected insurance and the storage of suitable fuels.

Fuel storage and the legislation caused insurance companies many problems and they in turn made things difficult for their clients, which ultimately restricted the growth and development of garages. The magazine was of the opinion that cars generally did not give value for money as they were subject to too many legal and material restraints, that they were unsafe and were unacceptable in terms of noise, odour and vibration. Several races and competitions were postponed in France and the United States for these or similar reasons. Commenting on the commemorative drive from Hyde Park to Brighton, *The*

Engineer stated, 'A number of the carriages were badly built foreign toys and could not be taken as representing engineering in earnest'. However, it also claimed that, 'the event was an unqualified, even magnificent success'.

The rules and entry form were published in *The Engineer* on 16 November 1896, with the event set for 31 May 1897. The competition was to be over two days, the first day being a series of tests carried out in front of a panel of judges, and the second a speed and endurance trial of 263 miles between Crystal Palace and the post office in Birmingham.

The competition and prize money were divided into four classes:

Class A. Best 4-seat, mechanically propelled vehicle of not more than 2 tons. Prize: 350gns.

Class B. Best 1, 2 or 3-seat, mechanically propelled vehicle of not more than 1 ton. Prize: 250gns.

Class C. Best mechanically propelled vehicle for a driver and up to 2 tons of freight. Prize: 250gns.

Class D. Best mechanically propelled vehicle for a driver and up to 1 ton of freight. Prize: 150gns.

A further prize of 100 guineas was offered for the best passenger or freight vehicle propelled by an engine running on oil or spirit with a specific gravity of less than 0.8 or a flash point lower than 73° F.

Percy Petter's reference to the motor competition in his history of 1933 does not truly record the facts. He states that in the preliminary days before the trial several distinguished engineers were given rides through the grounds of Crystal Palace and that when, finally, the great day for the run through England arrived, the participants were shattered by the notice board announcing cancellation of the event due to so few entries. He also suggests that Petters could have done with the £1,000 prize. The maximum amount they could have won was 350 guineas, the prize for their class of 250 guineas and 100 guineas if they were awarded the special prize for the best vehicle operating on fuel with a flashpoint of less than 73°F.

The official account of the event in *The Engineer* of 4 June 1897 is rather different from Percy's. A total of seventy-two entries had been received, including the one from the Yeovil Motor Car & Cycle Co., formed by James B. Petter with £1,000 capital and with a factory in his garden at Reckleford, represented by Petters' light business carriage for two in Class B.

Unfortunately, on the day of the event, just five entries arrived to take part in the trial. These were the four-seat petro-car and petro-cycle from Rootes & Venables; a steam van from Liquid Fuel & Engineering Co., from the Isle of

The Yeovil Motor Car & Cycle Co. entry by Petters in the 1897 Crystal Palace motor car competition organized by *The Engineer*. The car was powered by a 3 hp twin cylinder oil engine

Wight; the Bushbury electric cart from the Electric Construction Company, Wolverhampton; a light oil-powered car from a Mr Cornell; and the Petter entry.

Development at Yeovil had progressed during the two years separating the experimental car and the competition. The company had produced twelve cars and a new two-cylinder engine specifically for the car business. The vehicle entered in the competition was listed as being powered by a two-cylinder Petter Patent petroleum engine, the same name given to the company's range of agricultural power units. The two cylinders were arranged side by side to fire alternatively, the ignition being supplied by two ignition tubes heated by a single blowlamp. Driving could commence within ten minutes from cold with the engine running on Royal Daylight paraffin.

The inlet valves were operated by suction from the descending pistons and the exhaust valves actuated by levers driven from the crankshaft. Speeds of 4 or 10 mph could be attained depending on which of the two gears was selected.

Driving could be difficult depending on ground conditions as power was only to one of the rear wheels. The vehicle was still carriage-like in appearance, with two large wheels at the rear and tiller steering to the smaller front wheels.

Heavy rain during the week prior to the competition caused the landscaped 2 mile-long, hilly course with tight bends to become soft in parts. Some of the competition vehicles lost traction in these areas of soft ground, forcing their passengers to get out and push. Percy Petter and his mechanic, Herbert Swetman, had brought the car from Yeovil and like the other contestants were required to explain the construction of their vehicle to the judging panel followed by a simple test as directed by the judges. The test consisted of starting, stopping, turning, etc., and this was completed by all five of the competitors; the judges retired to an adjacent hut for a meeting that lasted half an hour.

Graham Harris, the Hon. Secretary, eventually emerged from the meeting to read a prepared statement, it was then pinned to the door of the hut indicating the termination of the preceedings. The statement read: 'The judges have decided that they cannot award a prize to any of the cars exhibited. It will therefore not be necessary for the trial run to Birmingham to take place'. The statement continued, 'Although the judges cannot see their way to award any

The 1897 Petter electric carriage taking part in the London Lord Mayor's Show

prizes, the steam car of the Liquid Fuel Engineering Co. and the Bushbury Electric Car of the Electric Construction Co. are highly commended'.

Understandably, there was considerable discussion among the five entrants who were dissatisfied with the outcome of the competition. The Electric Construction Co. and Rootes decided to drive their vehicles to Birmingham on the following day as planned and invited *The Engineer* magazine to witness the event. The route the two vehicles took was by way of St Albans, Dunstable, Stony Stratford, Towcester, Daventry and Coventry and was completed at an average speed of 8 mph. They reported that crowds of people were present at each town to witness the event and that no undue stoppages occurred.

Percy Petter returned to the Somerset factory to face a very disgruntled father. The profit from the sale of the custom-made cars and vans produced during the previous two years was gone and almost all of the £1,000 capital.

This was not quite the end to Petters' entry into the world of vehicle manufacture, for the company had been approached before the competition by a firm of battery makers with the request for two electrically propelled vehicles. These were made to everyone's satisfaction with two electric motors providing the power to each vehicle. There followed a request for a further three for a German customer of the battery maker with the order coming direct. The order stipulated that one vehicle was required to take part in the London Lord Mayor's Show on 9 November 1897. The vehicle was completed and took part in the show with a favourable comment reported in *The Times* newspaper. However, its brakes proved to be faulty as a result of Percy's error in folding the linings the wrong way so that they opened out when the brakes were applied instead of tightening. This defect caused the customer to cancel the order and refuse payment although Petters were prepared to rectify the error without charge. The Yeovil Motor Car & Cycle Co. was abandoned at this point in favour of stationary engines, leading to the misconception about which development came first.

CHAPTER THREE

1897–1904

Cheapness Born of Excellence

Among the company's early visitors to the Smithfield Show in 1896 were William and James Keenan from Dublin. Petters had been convinced that they should sell direct to the public via shows but the Keenans convinced them that volume sales in Ireland could only be achieved through agents. The Keenans were appointed and became responsible for many hundreds of engine sales. Percy married their sister, Emily Keenan; there was two sons and four daughters from that marriage. Following Emily's death, Percy married Ruth Penson-Harris; there were no children from this union and his wife survived him.

The Royal Show of 1897 featured 'Petter Patent Petroleum Oil Engines' on stand 87, consisting of a 5 hp engine driving a water pump, a 2.5 hp engine powering a dynamo and a 1 hp basic engine; R.A. Lister agricultural equipment was also shown on the stand as the two firms often intertraded. By 1903, Petter Handyman engines were also sold with a Lister name plate, no doubt leading to Listers making a petrol engine in 1908, having purchased the Stover design from Illinois, sold in the UK by F.C. Southwell & Co. of South London, which was purchased by Listers.

The prosperity in the general engineering industry prevented several well-known names from exhibiting at the Royal Show that year and the machinery press noted the lack of new machines. The trade's excuse was that it had neither the time nor the necessity to attempt to design new products. The established engine manufacturers of the day included: Richard Hornsby & Co.; Crossley Bros; Fielding & Platt Ltd; Tangyes Ltd; Campbell Gas Engine Co.; Robey & Co.; Proctor & Co.; J.& F. Howard; Clayton & Shuttleworth; the Trusty Engine Co.; R. Stephenson & Co.; and Greenwood & Batley, and were noted by *The Engineer* as guilty of producing engines little different from one another.

The front cover of the oldest surviving Petter engine brochure, *c.* 1903

However, the magazine did mention that those engine companies with something new to exhibit included Greenwood & Batley, Capel & Co., and the newcomer, James B. Petter & Sons.

According to Percy's family history, he, in conjunction with Messrs John and Harry Helyar, produced a small motorcycle in 1897, which he claimed was the first in Britain. Unfortunately, no other mention or photographs seem to exist so this cannot be confirmed.

All five of James's sons were now in leading roles within the company. As the boys grew older and more experienced, they became anxious to demonstrate their management skills; James would hear nothing of this and refused to attend meetings they called to discuss improvements and the general running of the various departments. He declared his right to veto any decisions they made at the meetings if he disagreed. The eldest and youngest sons, Harry and Hugh, assisted their father in his ironmongery business while the second son, Guy, carried out the clerical and secretarial work with Percy in the foundry and engineering works. Percy's twin brother, Ernest, had a head for accountancy and financial matters which led him to leave home to open the company's London office and showroom in 1899. He was successful there right from the beginning, as the following story illustrates.

A rare photograph of a Petter Handyman (*c.* 1906) with a Lister agency nameplate

A 'city gent', attired in frock coat and striped trousers, fell over some engine crates being unloaded outside the showroom and, furious, shouted that he was going to sue the company for £1,000 in damages. His cries of pain and wrath summoned Ernest who calmed him down and after ascertaining there was little damage done, assured him there was no point in litigation as the company did not have such a sum. The gent enquired what was in the cases and on hearing they were oil engines, asked if they would be any good for driving printing machines in India. He was the owner of Caslon & Co., the printing machine manufacturers, and when assured that the engines were ideal for that purpose, he purchased one.

Shortly after that incident, H.M. Stanley, the explorer, walked into the showroom enquiring, 'Where is the chief thief of this concern?' Ernest's reaction was to call for 'the fellow to be turned out'. After identities were established, it transpired that Stanley was trying to drain a lake on his estate and to date all contractors had let him down. Ernest sent his chief mechanic, Herbert Swetman, to the estate and he reported that there was no problem and the job could be completed in six weeks. Stanley was in the vicinity when

Ernest and the mechanic started the engine pump for the first time and witnessed only a small amount of water being discharged. 'Cheated, cheated, robbed again,' shouted Stanley, who was promptly told to go away by Ernest and return when things had been sorted out. Stanley did so and was overjoyed a few hours later when Ernest went up to the house to fetch him to see the full flow of water being pumped. The lake was emptied well inside the agreed time and Stanley became an ardent supporter of Petters.

Percy became increasingly worried at the factory's poor production rate due to lack of space and insufficient money for new equipment. He got into conversation with his good friend R.A. Lister, and this led to Percy being invited to Dursley. He stayed at Lister's home, and was encouraged to learn that better banking could be available. Stuckey's (now NatWest) were Petters' bank and had been for many years but they would only offer £1,500 overdraft; all attempts to increase that amount failed.

As suggested by Lister, Percy approached the Wilts & Dorset Bank (now Lloyds) with a request for a £7,000 overdraft. After referral to head office, the request was granted providing Petters changed banks. The change led to severe disagreement with James B. Petter for he was a personal friend of the manager of Stuckey's Bank and found the large overdraft very disconcerting.

With the new finance, the twins launched forth on bigger and better production of engines and participation in exhibitions. The euphoria was short-lived, however, for at the end of May 1901 Percy was recalled from the Bath and West Show to be told by the auditors that the annual accounts showed a loss of £3,000. James B. Petter was furious and maintained the engine division, and Percy in particular, had ruined all of them. His daily outbursts became worse and he openly went around broadcasting that he and the company were bankrupt. In fact, some years previously, James had been seriously misled by some well-meaning stocktaker friends who had overestimated the stock level. Now, under new management, the stock had been written down to a conservative level, which of course created a substantial reduction in the balance sheet.

James instructed Ernest and Percy to cease engine production immediately, which neither could accept. Shortly after this, Percy suggested that he and his brother purchase the engine division to operate on their own. James was of the opinion that this was just another of Percy's wildcat schemes, but eventually agreed. A written sale offer of £3,850 was reluctantly signed by James with a one month option to purchase.

Percy took the train to London to meet Ernest to discuss ways of raising £5,000, the purchase price plus operating capital. Ernest was bitter because he had previously started a country produce to London business which showed

Sir Ernest W. Petter on the left and his
twin brother Percival W. Petter, *c.* 1910

every sign of success. Unfortunately, father did not like the sound of it and
ordered the venture to close. Due to his father's previous attitude, Ernest wanted
the engine business to close, so enabling Percy and him to start afresh. However,
Percy finally persuaded him to agree to the purchase and both started to raise
the money. The twins had only £300 between them, having been paid no more
than £2 per week each since completing their apprenticeship.

Their mother's religious friends and Ernest's new found 'city' benefactors
came to their aid, raising £4,000 before the time limit, despite their father
trying to call off the deal. The £4,000 was enough to purchase and pay legal
fees, leaving just £75 as working capital! Percy had wanted the new company to
be called Petter Bros. Ltd but a cousin in Barnstaple had previously lost a
business by that name, so that was ruled out. James B. Petter & Sons Ltd, was
formed with Dr W.R. Moore, a religious friend from South Molton, as
chairman, a position he retained until resigning over Petters' manufacturing
munitions in 1915.

Work commenced on a new Nautilus engine factory in the Reckleford area

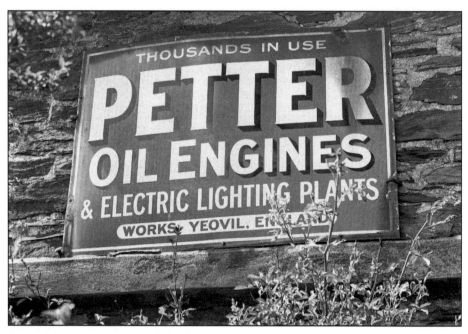

A typical Petter vitreous-enamelled advertising sign used on railway embankments and platforms, *c.* 1920/30

of Yeovil and the new company's first trading year showed a profit of £2,000. At last James B. Petter retired and moved to Bristol to recover from the nervous breakdown he suffered as a result of the near bankruptcy. He returned to Yeovil in later years to live in West Park.

Engine sales were promoted by vitreous-enamelled advertising signs on railway embankments or station buildings and became a traditional part of London's railway sidings and many provincial stations. 'Petter Oil Engines' became known throughout the world; in fact, in many parts of Africa the name became a generic term for any green painted engine. One of the enamelled signs was found in 1973 virtually holding a wall together at a disused station on the Isle of Man's railway to a silver-lead mine in the Slieu Whallin mountains!

Ernest and Percy were often mistaken for each other. Percy was quieter than the extrovert Ernest and did not drink or smoke, the absence of tobacco stains being one of the quicker forms of identification. The brothers were Anglican, although Percy also followed his mother's interest in the Christian Brethren. Shortly before Ernest's death in 1954, he turned to the Brethren faith, declaring he had at last 'found God'. They held strong views on national topics and were not slow to air them in writing. In 1925 Ernest wrote *The Disease of Unemployment and the Cure*, while between 1922 and 1947 Percy wrote six books. These were *The Story of the Pilgrim Preachers and Their Message*, followed by *Assembly Service*, on the Assemblies of the Open Brethren, 1930; *The Counsel of Sapiens*, 1939; *Eternal Life – The Gift of God*, 1942; and *Guilty Clergy*, 1943. His last book was *Essential Amendments in the Canon Law*, proposed for the Church of England in the Report of the Archbishop's Commission on Canon Law, 1947. Percy was President of the National Union of Protestants when he died.

Guy, Ernest and Percy filed thirty-nine patents between 1898 and 1918. Most of them related to engine improvements, including the exhaust-heated ignition tube in 1900, which did away with constant-flame ignition.

In 1902 a 5 hp self-propelled unit resembling a traction engine was announced; it could haul 2 ton loads over reasonably level ground or pull a small plough or binder. The method of water-cooling was by a crankshaft-driven rotary pump spraying water on to baffle plates in the engine's chimney, the upward air current cooling the water temperature. The road speed was 2 or 4 mph, depending on the gear selected, and braking was by traditional screw blocks to the rear wheels. A later version was marketed as the 'Petter Patent Traction Engine', and one of these named 'Intrepid' was used in Yeovil for hauling removal vans or cartloads of castings between the Petter foundry and their factories.

Petter employees formed a dramatic society, a hockey team with several county players, and the famous football team, Petters United. The team's biggest success was the 7–1 defeat of Yeovil Town in 1913/14, leading to calls for the teams to be amalgamated so as to take the town higher in the football league.

In 1903 strong competition for Petters' oil engines came from an American company, Fairbanks Morse, who were supposedly taking large orders for their 2 hp petrol engine 'Jack-of-all-Trades' at the county shows.

Petters were reluctant to drop their prices or lower standards to cheapen the product as durability had become a byword. Crankshafts were machined from solid billets of steel instead of welded sections and Petters' proportionate governing, using metered air and fuel at every stroke depending on engine load, provided steam engine-like smoothness. Most of the competition used 'hit and miss' governing, with its ferocity often leading to component failure. Petters decided that a new approach was necessary.

Previously, their engines had been heavy units designed for stationary, permanent site operation. To combat the competition, they designed a new range of lighter, portable engines specifically for the farmer and agricultural

A self-propelled oil traction engine produced by Petters *c.* 1902

estate. Using the same horizontal cylinder design with lighter construction the 2.25 hp Handyman was launched. To overcome the suggestion of inferiority to the continuing standard range, the sales literature carried the slogan 'Cheapness in the Petter Sense, is Cheapness Born of Excellence'. In fact, the Handyman series were some 20 per cent lower in price than the standard range and won the company its first silver medal at the 1903 Staffordshire Show.

The following Bath and West Show saw Petters exhibiting the Handyman as a special model being sold by Mr Wakley, who was an American temporary employee, and well versed in sales techniques. His idea to sell the Handyman only to agents and stockists in batches of fifty or more paid off, for by the end of the show Petters had orders for over four hundred engines. The range was increased to include 3.5 hp and 5 hp models; later, 8 hp and 10 hp versions were added. Factory resources had to be reorganized for the current production was running at only twenty engines per week. Percy decided to embarked on a series of tours throughout the British Isles establishing a network of agents.

The date of Petters' first export is not known with certainty, but in 1905 a 1.5 hp Handyman was sent to a customer in South America. He reordered some eighteen years later, with a request for three 100 hp engines and a note saying he was so pleased with the first engine that he again wanted to buy from the company.

A Petter Handyman oil engine presented by the author to the London Science Museum, *c.* 1966

Listers and Petters continued to exchange products. Petters sold Listers' 'Melotte' cream separators and Listers put their own nameplates on Handyman engines. Listers became active in electrical generation in 1903, acquiring firms making dynamos and switchgear two years later. When they started to make Southwell petrol engines the intertrading with Petters ceased and was not revived for nearly eighty years. Petters dropped the 'Melotte' cream separator and bought a design from the Earl of Ilchester's agent, Howell Wells, to make their own and other items of dairy equipment.

At the Royal Show of 1903, a William Newbold Baines asked if he could represent Petters in Russia. Ernest appointed him on a 5 per cent commission-only basis, whereupon Baines sold for about 10 per cent more than home prices and soon earned more than Ernest and Percy combined. The Russians wanted engines of the two-stroke design capable of running on low-grade fuel so Petters studied the Swedish Bolinder design and produced their 'S' series in 1909. The 'S' series became famous for its reliability and low cost of operation, earning the company a gold medal in Brussels in 1910 and the Grand Prix of Turin in 1911.

The sales of Petters' traction oil engines to Russia and surrounding countries were good but the vehicles did not sell well in the UK, despite considerable publicity and demonstrations of endurance.

CHAPTER FOUR

1905–13
Westland Affair

Major additions to the 3 acre Nautilus factory at the junction of Reckleford and Gold Croft included a foundry, powerhouse, office block, assembly/machine workshops and a packing department. The architects were John Petter and his partner Percy Warren, who produced a fine building at a cost that almost exhausted the company's resources, so in 1910 they went public. Petters Ltd was floated with a share capital of £150,000. The board comprised Dr William R. Moore, chairman; Ernest Petter, managing director; Percy W. Petter and Guy B. Petter, and John Vincent, JP, as directors. The new works were a great success, with the foundry going into twenty-four hour production from day one, the two cupolas working alternate days to keep the molten metal flowing. The nonstop rate of castings enabled the increased workforce of some five hundred to boost engine production to around 1,500 units per year.

As the export market grew there was a need for overseas service engineers; these talented men, many of them ex-Petter apprentices, often travelled to remote places to carry out installations, warranty checks or major overhauls. To undertake those journeys at the turn of the century sometimes required the use of pack-mules and canoes. Charlie Munden was one such engineer working in British Columbia calling on mining and logging camps; many years later, he became Petters' service manager based at Hamble.

Herbert Brooks, another young service engineer just out of apprenticeship in 1910, found himself installing an electrical generating set on a Russian cruiser in Scapa Flow. He excelled himself and showed a flair for working with Russians so Petters assigned him to William Baines as an assistant. One trip required him to go to St Petersburg to maintain an 'S' type engine undergoing cold weather trials. The trials lasted for some weeks and each night the engine was sealed by the examiners to prevent adjustments or parts being changed. Eventually satisfied with the engine's performance, the Russians awarded Petters a silver medal for their product. The introduction of the 'S' type led to even more remote installations.

An artist's impression of the Nautilus engine works at Reckleford, Yeovil, *c.* 1912

Many of the applications were for the larger power units running for extended hours without supervision at up to 12,000 ft powering wireless telegraphy stations in South America. The engine's ability to run on heavy crude naphtha or similar low grade fuel, developed for the Russian market, had brought Petters to the attention of the South American authorities. The quality of Petter engines became a legend; each was tested, and a signed certificate, usually by Guy Petter, issued quoting the performance. Proud owners framed these magnificent certificates and hung them in their engine houses.

In the early sixties, the author was given an original test certificate for a P2D dated 30 October 1911. It had been discovered by a service engineer in Africa. As I shared the birth date with the P2D, but not the year, I felt obliged to try to recover the engine for the company's valuable museum collection. With the aid of Bob Jones, the overseas service supervisor for the area, we traced it to a farm in Bulawayo where it was photographed with the owner's adult son standing next to it surrounded by crops. The engine was still in working order and much prized by the family, so with difficulty, by dint of an exchange and cash, we managed to obtain it.

The long journey home to Staines and the change of climate followed by an unfortunate wait before apprentices could begin the restoration, hastened the disintegration of the wheeled chassis. Eventually, restored and together with a photographic display of its story and the test certificate, the engine formed the centrepiece of Petters' stand at the Royal Show, Stoneleigh, in 1969. The original certificate is still in my personal collection of Petter memorabilia.

The 'S' type semi-diesel engines designed by Zacharia Hall operated at high temperature and so were fitted with water-cooled cylinder heads. Imitations of

A Certificate is sent out with each Engine when first despatched from the works.
If lost or destroyed it cannot be renewed.

Certificate of Test.

This is to Certify

that the   Petter   Engine, Registered № 22415
size P2D   Type   Portable   has been
manufactured at the   Nautilus Works, Yeovil, in
accordance with our latest design and practice and has
been carefully tested for a working load of 11½   Brake
Horse Power at   300   Revolutions per minute.
     The Engine has been examined for defects, all parts
specially inspected and passed as satisfactory in all respects
     It is sent out from these Works under the following

Guarantee

     We undertake to supply, free of charge new parts to
replace any which may break or show undue wear
on account of defective material or workmanship
within twelve months after delivery, provided such
parts are sent for inspection to our Works.   We do
not accept responsibility for consequential damages
under any circumstances whatever.
     When ordering spare parts the above Registered Number
which is also stamped on the Engine should be quoted.

Dated Nautilus Works, Yeovil, October 30th. 1911.

Signed on behalf of
the Directors of
Petters Limited.

             Guy B Petter   Director.

To be framed and hung up in the Engine Room.

Engine Test Certificate No. 22415, 30 October 1911

Petter P2D No. 22415 still operating in Zimbabwe in 1965 with the son of the original owner

them were made by competitors who used water 'injection' instead of the water-cooled heads. This sometimes caused failure of bearings or the crankshaft so Petters published several warnings to customers to beware of the imitations. The smooth two-stroke operation of the 'S' was extremely quiet, sometimes likened to a steam engine. This quiet running on Russian naphtha, Scottish shale, Texan resoleum and Admiralty fuel oil or similar low-grade fuels, costing 1*d* for 8 hp, made them popular throughout the world.

In the spring of 1965, the author found an 'S' type still operating at a coffin-maker's sawmill on Bodmin Moor. The 18 hp engine, built in 1918, had been used to drive a 48 in diameter circular saw converting elm trunks into planks. The old engine stood deep in sawdust with oxygen/acetylene bottles leaning against it, having been retired for a more modern power unit with electric start. Only one flywheel remained, the other having departed through the corrugated wall of the sawmill some forty years earlier when the crankshaft broke. The local blacksmith had reversed the crankshaft and refitted the drive pulleys on the opposite end. After much rummaging about in the ankle-deep sawdust beneath

The return to Petters' Staines factory of the Zimbabwe P2D, *c.* 1966, having been purchased by the author for the company museum

a bench, the owner proudly held out the broken portion of the crankshaft for me to see.

On enquiring whether the engine was in running order, I was rewarded by the owner lighting a brazing torch and placing it against the cylinder head; not the recommended method of starting but an effective one, for within five minutes the old engine was idling away as if it had never ceased to operate.

The 'S' range was produced in thirteen sizes from 8 hp at 375 r/min to the massive 200 hp at 285 r/min, and sold at £131 for the 8 hp model and £1,470 for the largest in the range.

Problems of space hampered the Nautilus works, as there was no further room for development. The foundry needed more outside space for weathering castings, and this created shortages in the assembly shop. It was obvious that more production space was required if deliveries were not to become affected. During a discussion concerning casting shortages, Mr Hardyman, the foundry manager, suggested to Percy Petter that a new site was required with its own railway sidings so that raw material could be delivered by rail. Pig iron was still being transported by road from the local station where it had arrived by rail from Southampton Docks.

The idea was not received with too much enthusiasm but shortly afterwards the manager asked Percy to accompany him to a site at West Hendford. The site was a meadow adjoining the GWR Yeovil to Taunton branch line, so there was a possibility of connecting sidings. The Petter board agreed to purchase the site plus some additional land amounting to an area of 75 acres. A small private company was formed to develop the site as a garden village designed by John Petter and his partner Percy Warren, along the lines of the successful Cadbury Bournville scheme.

The scheme called for employees' houses to be set in a rural estate with the new foundry close at hand. One Saturday in 1913, Percy and his wife, with daughters Nora and Kathleen, cut the first sods for the foundry which became operational early the next year. It was Percy's wife Emily who suggested the name of Westland for the new factory as it was located to the west of the town.

The Nautilus works had been the subject of a visit by *The Engineer* the previous year followed by a review published on 5 April 1912. The wisdom of transporting pig-iron from Middlesborough via sea, rail and road to the Yeovil works was questioned but by the same token the review confirmed Petters' Nautilus foundry as one of the most up-to-date, with an average weekly output of 40 tons of castings ranging from a ½ oz to 4 tons. The good natural lighting, provided by north lights in the roof, was also commented upon. In fact, these had been placed there to prevent the moulding sand from drying out prematurely on warm sunny days! However, the company did provide adequate illumination for the foundry workers in the form of five mercury vapour lights each of 5,000 candle power; all the plant's electricity supply came from Petters' own power station.

The factory employed six hundred people working a 56 hour week in accordance with the Factory Act of 1874.

The pattern shop and engine erection hall quickly followed the completion of the Westland foundry. The area designated for the garden village was surveyed, laid out and the building of the first four houses started.

Petters' range of products was still increasing, with direct reversing marine semi-diesels of 38 to 300 hp being made for civil, commercial and admiralty craft. Yet another agricultural tractor had been produced in 1911, from which considerable publicity was gained. The tractor bearing the registration plate of YC4 pulled an 8 ton load of engines from Yeovil to Thame for the Oxfordshire Show, a distance of 125 miles, in 24 hours for only 30 gallons of fuel. It continued after the show to Salisbury and, later, Cardiff for similar events. This

A 1918 'S' type 18 hp oil engine still operational in a Cornish coffin-makers in 1966

A 1911 Petter 30 hp oil engine tractor

was the first of many such feats to promote Petters' new Plough tractor works, also built on the Westland site.

The 1911 tractor's engine had a massive 10¾ in bore with a 12 in stroke and operated at 300 r/min to drive a power take-off (pto) or the 60 in rear wheels at 2½ to 5 mph. The spiral-wound radiator consisted of 180 ft of copper tube and required 3 gallons of water per day. The machine weighed 5 tons and could haul its 14 ft 9 in length and a load of 10 tons up 1:10 gradients. In the following year the bore was increased to 11¾ in diameter, raising the power to 35 hp, and the rear wheels were enlarged to 20 in wide, so making ploughing easier with the increased power.

There was considerable jubilation in the town and within the firm when Petters gained a Parliamentary Order to supply Yeovil with electricity in 1913. However, problems developed when the site for the power station in Dampier Street proved too small to house the Petter generating-sets (gen-sets). Negotiations to acquire more land adjacent to the plot proved fruitless as there was a school close to it. When the First World War started, the project was shelved, although the Order was kept alive and eventually made over to the Yeovil Electric Light & Power Co.

The impressive list of satisfied users grew steadily, with the Crown Agents for the Colonies, the India Office, the War Office, the Office of Works and the

Commission of Woods and Forests all being added. The list of foreign government buyers also increased, no doubt as a result of the company's exhibition participation in France, Holland, Belgium, Italy, Russia and South Africa.

The tireless efforts of William Baines in Russia led to his appointment as a director of the company in 1912. Unfortunately, he died five years later, having caught influenza in an epidemic that swept Russia.

A strange event took place in the North Sea in 1913 that affected Petters some years later. Rudolph Diesel, the German inventor, mysteriously disappeared from the Harwich to Hamburg ferry. He was returning after a routine visit to Ipswich where his company, Consolidated Diesel Engine Manufacturing Ltd, was building a massive factory. The factory was designed for quantity manufacture of diesel engines for submarines and work on the 46 acre site was almost complete. Following the death of Rudolph Diesel, the project was immediately shelved and the factory remained closed. Could Diesel's death have been an attempt to stop manufacture of a product with enemy munitions potential being made in England?

CHAPTER FIVE

1914–18

Wings of War

From the turn of the century things changed in the Petter family. The eldest son, Harry, left the foundry to emigrate to Alberta, Canada, and Hugh became a missionary in Buenos Aires. With the two sons gone, the ironmongery business in the High Street was sold to Hill & Sawtell in 1909, with Petters retaining an interest in it until the early fifties. The Nautilus stove and grate business was represented in London by John Line & Sons of Tottenham Court Road until its sale to the Davis Gas Stove Co. in 1914. Castings for all Petter products had been made in the company's Yeovil foundry or supplied by Hadens of Trowbridge until 1912 when they ceased to trade. It was for that reason that Petters built their own foundry on the Nautilus site in three months during the same year and appointed Hardyman as manager.

Richard C. Petter, the youngest brother, joined the family firm in 1908 to commence a four-year apprenticeship, which was followed by a year's further training with the giant machine tool company, Alfred Herbert Ltd. He continued his studies in Germany with two years at the Bremen technical college but the political scene was deteriorating and he returned home in March 1914. On rejoining Petters, he was given charge of the Junior engine assembly shop where the 5 hp unit was being made; the 1½ and 3 hp units were added later.

Britain declared war on Germany on 4 August 1914. It came as no great shock for most people had considered it inevitable and that the conflict would soon be over.

Percy Petter was on holiday with his family in Minehead when the news broke and he received an urgent message to return to Yeovil where a War Office official was waiting to see him. Apparently, the government were anxious about German submarine activity and the vulnerability of the Forth Bridge into Scotland. It was felt that searchlights mounted on the shoreline would act as a deterrent and the War Office wanted Petters to design and make several high–

The Petter Westland factory as it was in 1918

powered gen-sets. Within three days the required number of large engines had been coupled to dynamos and the searchlights sent on their long journey north.

Mass enlistment in the army or navy by young, single men took place. 'We'll be home by Christmas' was the cry as they left their families and places of employment. Richard Petter joined the Royal Fusiliers on 9 August as a private but re-enlisted shortly after in the Royal Naval Air Service where he became a pilot and attained the rank of captain a year later. He was shot down and taken prisoner at Ostend in September 1915. He was later transferred to Holland where he eventually met and married his wife.

With many of their craftsmen enlisting in the armed forces, Petters could have been in difficulty with production had not export orders been cancelled from several countries. Nevertheless, a certain amount of reorganization within the factory took place. Sadly, the board decided that the Nautilus grates were no longer required, so the name and production rights were sold.

With the outbreak of hostilities, all the money owing to Petters from the sale of engines in Russia was paid into the National Bank; the absence of this considerable sum made financial difficulties for the company, so they were more than pleased when the British government declared a moratorium on debts.

The immediate effect of the war on industry was very little except for the sudden shortage of young men. Another early military order received by Petters was for Gen. Sir John French's mobile command vehicle to be fitted with a gen-set for lighting. Gen. French was commander-in-chief of the British Expeditionary Force that landed in France on 8 August 1914.

Soon Britain was facing an increasing shortage of raw materials as a result of German submarine attacks on shipping. The true state of affairs was not generally known as the information was withheld from the press. Industry slowly became aware of the effects when changes in specifications occurred

Capt. Richard C. Petter, *c.* 1918

without warning and standards started to fall, leading to a general lack of quality control. When deliveries started to be affected in early 1915, Lloyd George, the recently appointed Minister for Munitions, had to reveal to Parliament the true state of the country.

The minister called for immediate help from industry to meet the increasing demands of war. The Petter board of directors called an emergency meeting on 27 April 1915, at which they passed the following resolution: 'In view of the expressed need of the country, the manufacturing capacity of the company shall be forthwith offered to the Government for the purpose of making munitions of War, or otherwise as required'.

The chairman of the board, Dr W.R. Moore, resigned as a matter of religious conscience as he felt he could not be associated with mass manufacture of weapons. His loss to the company was deeply felt for he had been a major shareholder and investor since the twins' purchase of the engine division in 1901. Immediately after the meeting, Dr Moore asked J.R. Seward, company secretary, to dispose of his Ordinary and Preference Shares at par to any

The first aircraft to be built by Petters in 1916, a Short 225/184 seaplane

interested employee. The shares were sold at the current rate of 32*s* 6*d* (£1.62½p) and 26*s* (£1.30p) respectively. Ernest Petter became chairman of the company.

A copy of the resolution was sent to the War Office and the admiralty; the latter replied with a telegram calling a meeting and requesting two representatives to attend. Percy and Ernest made their way to the admiralty where they learned of the country's urgent need for seaplanes. The admiralty felt that as Petters operated a large foundry, they also had a number of pattern-makers and they would be ideal to make aeroplanes!

A second meeting was quickly arranged by the admiralty for Petters to visit Short Bros. at Rochester, Kent, to see the type of aircraft required. Shorts were already producing seaplanes and Oswald Short gave Percy Petter and Percy Warren, the ex-architect, a guided tour of the plant. The meeting finished and they left the building with a contract to build twelve 'Two-Two-Five' Short 184 seaplanes and wondering to what they had committed the company. On the following day at Petters' Westland site a small party of men walked across a field to where a hut stood. They paused, and Ernest Petter opened the door proclaiming, 'This is the Westland aircraft works'.

Initially, John Petter and Percy Warren were placed in charge of the project but few of the workforce had seen an aircraft at close quarters and none had airframe construction experience. It was obvious that a qualified aeronautical engineer would have to be found to train and supervise the team. Fortunately, Percy Petter possessed a good memory and recalled having interviewed a Robert A. Bruce a year or so earlier for a managerial position in the Nautilus works. Bruce had been a manager with British & Colonial Aeroplane Co., so Percy was able to trace him via the Institution of Mechanical Engineers.

Petters managed to obtain Bruce's release from the Sopwith Aviation Co. at Kingston where, as a lieutenant in the navy, he had been seconded as an

Robert A. Bruce, Petter Westland
managing director, *c.* 1920

admiralty aircraft inspector. Bruce joined the Westland aircraft division of Petters as manager in June 1915. Construction of the first 'Two-Two-Fives' commenced in August, with the small team headed by Bruce virtually learning on the job. The team consisted of John Petter, Percy Warren, Arthur Davenport, F.J. Perry, R.G. Dellow and a Mr Seaman. By Christmas, two aircraft were complete except for 'doping' of the wing and fuselage fabric, causing delivery to be put back until January 1916. Bruce later brought in an old colleague from his days with Brennan torpedos, Robert J. Norton, as his clerical assistant who later became commercial and engineering manager.

The engine works also churned out thousands of eighteen pounder shell cases and many gun carriages. As the war progressed, the drain on factory labour continued, with some four hundred of Petters' young men joining the armed forces. Older men and women from all walks of life were recruited from a wide area around Yeovil and trained in new skills. Bruce's wife became one of the first women to work in an aircraft factory when she took up the task of marking out wing assembly jigs.

Two examples of Petter female employees engaged in aircraft production; the 1917–18 photo (top) illustrates some of the first women in aircraft manufacture while the 1940 photo (bottom) shows them making parts for Spitfire MkV aircraft that Westland produced for a short period

Slowly, the Petter team involved in aircraft construction were coming together and the firm's past name for quality and engineering excellence in engines began to show in its new-found aerial products.

An example of this relates to HMS *Engadine*, a seaplane carrier serving with the First Battle Cruiser Squadron. The ship carried several 'Two-Two-Five' planes built by various companies under licence from Shorts; one of them, No. 8359, was built by Petters at Yeovil and had become regarded as 'dependable'. When the cruiser squadron sighted the enemy off Jutland, an aircraft was ordered to carry out reconnaissance. Flight Commander F.J. Rutland RN decided to fly the mission himself and selected No. 8359 instead of his usual

The second seaplane order, for Short Canton Unne aircraft to be built by Petters in 1916, required assembly and testing on the Hamble, Southampton

plane. The flight lasted 45 minutes and was entirely successful, making the Petter-built aircraft the first plane to be involved in a major sea battle, for the Battle of Jutland was soon to commence. The aircraft was later consigned to London's Imperial War Museum where it was severely damaged in an air raid in 1940; the fuselage was restored after the Second World War by the Fleet Air Arm and is now part of their museum collection at RNAS Yeovilton – only a few miles from where it was originally built. On completion of the 'Two-Two-Five' contract, Petters were required to build Short Canton Unne seaplanes and Sopwith 'One-and-a-Half' strutter biplane fighters. As each aircraft was completed and passed inspection, they were dismantled and packed into crates for rail transit to Hamble, Southampton, where they were reassembled and test flown.

In 1916 Avro Aircraft Co. acquired 200 acres of land at Hamble on which they constructed an aircraft factory and airfield with slipway to Southampton Water; most of their work related to experimental projects based on the 504 aircraft. Harry Fairhurst, a Manchester architect, was brought in to design and build a 'garden city' of 350 houses but only 24 had been completed when the government took over the site. Gerard V. Roe became general manager of the Avro factory and later turned cleric to become the Revd G.V. Roe, vicar of Hamble Parish Church. Avros allowed Westland to assemble and test fly Short seaplanes from their slipway in 1917. One of the first people to fly from Hamble had been Winston Churchill in a Sopwith Tutor in 1913. He also received flying lessons there from Lt. D.A. Spencer-Gray, RN.

The 1917 Petter Iron Horse tractor

Following the first aircraft contracts, Petters received an order to build DH4 biplanes to be test flown on site. The Westland site had to be extended by Petters purchasing the Northover Fields from the Yeovil and District Hospital Board. After a considerable amount of hedge removal, draining and levelling was completed, a grass airfield was established and, in April 1917, the first DH4 built by Petters at Westland took off.

The plane was piloted by Barry C. Hucks, a pre-war aerobatic ace who was the first person to loop an aircraft in August 1910. All was well and on the following morning the aircraft was ready for delivery to France. The occasion was witnessed by a large crowd from the town, including an elderly alderman, who had insisted on rising from his deathbed to see the event. The intense excitement must have been good for him, for he continued to live to a ripe old age.

A Petter Westland-built DH9A biplane, *c.* 1917

The government was becoming increasingly worried as a major food shortage swept Britain in 1917, resulting in a controller of agriculture being appointed by the Ministry of Munitions. The people were urged to grow more food for themselves and industry was again asked to assist by designing labour-saving agricultural implements. Patriotic as ever, Petters designed a 10 hp engine-driven plough and exhibited it at the Smithfield Show. The strange design had the driver's seat cantilevered out behind the rear driving wheels, giving the appearance of a horse-drawn plough. In fact, the tractor was steered by 'reins' to the single front wheel, over which a direction arrow allowed the driver to 'see' where his front wheel was pointing.

The Westland site had plenty of room for expansion so the Plough works, which operated as a separate division of Petters, continued to design and develop implements to aid land cultivation, so speeding up the country's food production. So great was the need for home-grown food in 1917–18 that three million acres of grassland were cultivated throughout Britain to grow cereal crops, as previously the country had imported 80 per cent of its requirements.

Crops and food production were not the only shortages and government urged industrial suppliers to sub-contract orders when their own facilities could not meet demand. Petters, with their Westland foundry and ability to cast low-carbon crucible steel, became very busy with orders from the motor industry for castings of intricate design. It was fortunate that these orders brought in new revenue for the company lost the money previously placed in the Russian National Bank when the Bolshevik revolution took place in 1917.

Towards the end of 1917, Petters' Westland division began to experiment with aircraft designs of its own. The first Petter Westland designs were the N16 and N17, both single-seat biplanes with floats. These aircraft were the brainchild of

The 1918 Petter Victory 'M' type oil engine

Robert Bruce and featured a new device, a wing-cambering ability that had a similar effect to the modern wing-flap. Although successful, the design clashed with the development by other companies of carrier-based planes which were much faster and so the N16 and 17 were scrapped.

The production of 150 DH4s was completed and followed by a similar contract for DH9s. The DH9 aircraft were uprated with the 400 hp American Liberty engine and Petters undertook the task of converting the fuselage to take the larger power unit; when they entered service the aircraft were reclassified as DH9As. Over 400 DH9As were built by Petter Westland and helped to bring British air supremacy to the skies over the Western Front.

It was inevitable that the busy test aerodrome of Westland's would sooner or later experience its first flying accident. On 3 September 1917 an Avro two-seater flown by Fl. Lt. Thomas, RNAS, with Robert Norton as passenger, stalled on takeoff for Hendon. It crashed, killing the pilot and severely injuring the passenger. At first it was thought Norton would not walk again but after twelve months in hospital he returned to work.

Inside Petters' Westland foundry, *c.* 1918

The 'small' engine assembly line in Petters' Westland works, *c.* 1918

The 'heavy' engine shop of Petters' Westland factory, *c.* 1918

Regular deliveries of DH9As to the RAF's receiving depot at Dunkirk provided the troops with an ideal opportunity for supplementing their drink allowance. The aircraft were flown by shuttle pilots with no passenger or gun in the rear cockpit so ballasting had to be installed. It so happened that a 12 gallon cask of cider was the right size and weight for the ballast – no wonder the DH9As were a welcome sight!

In July 1918 Petters experienced what was possibly their worst labour dispute. The workforce of their Westland power station went on strike following the dismissal of a colleague for theft. The absence of power caused the remaining workforce of around three thousand to experience severe problems in carrying out their respective war effort tasks. All attempts to justify the dismissal failed and the government feared the dispute might spread to other engineering companies around the country, so it urged Petters to yield and reinstate the man. Percy Petter refused and eventually a government commission of inquiry was set up in Yeovil Town Hall. Percy conducted the case for the firm and a Mr Stuckey acted for the striking men.

The organized labour finally agreed to the dismissal providing that in future Petters negotiated with the Joint Works Committee on all matters relating to possible dispute. Unfortunately, Percy accepted, only to find that in a few days he was threatened with an instant strike over a foreman's reprimand concerning spoilt work. Stuckey wanted the matter referred to the committee but Percy could see this precedent would lead to complete disruption of the works. In turn, he suggested calling in the government commission again. Days passed and the labour force refused to back Stuckey in any further strike, so the matter died.

In mid-1918, Westland built the Wagtail, their own single-seat, scout biplane, but sadly only five were made as the engine developed trouble on test flights. The problem could have been overcome but thankfully the Armistice intervened on 11 November. The last military planes to be built at Yeovil were an order for seventy-five Vickers Vimy twin-engined bombers, the largest planes to be built in the First World War, and destined to bomb Berlin had the hostilities not finished. The contract was amended by the government to twenty-five aircraft.

Petters received payment from the government for the labour and materials expended on the twenty-five Vimys but nothing in terms of profit. The profit had been earmarked to pay for the construction of massive hangers required to house the bomber build programme, so once again the company saw heavy losses.

The small group of people at Petters' Westland factory who started to build aircraft under licence in 1915 had grown into a massive labour force. Their joint efforts had completed 808 aircraft comprising 774 land planes and 34 seaplanes. Not a bad record for an area lacking any previous industrial tradition!

CHAPTER SIX

1918–24

A Time for Change

The Royal Air Force, having been established on 1 April 1918, took over the role previously played by the Royal Flying Corps. When the First World War finished, the RAF had 200 squadrons and 22,647 aircraft at its disposal. With hostilities over, the 330 Petter employees who had enlisted started to come home; sadly, eighteen of them failed to return.

Like so many manufacturers after the war, Petters produced a product named 'Victory'; this was an addition to the Junior range of engines. But the vast aircraft hangers stayed empty when the last Vickers Vimy was rolled out for its test flight and departure. Faced with diminishing orders, the management searched hard for work to avoid laying off staff, some of whom had only just returned from the war. There were few military contracts being issued so when the admiralty asked Westland to design a deck-landing conversion for the DH9A the company reluctantly agreed, for Westland considered it would have been more efficient to design a new carrier-based plane. The admiralty, however, was convinced it was cheaper to carry out the conversion. The work was completed and the result was an ungainly aeroplane, the Walrus, that was vicious to fly, but the customer was happy and ordered thirty-six more DH9As to be converted. As aircraft work dried up, Petters turned to conventional, if unusual, products.

They designed a 'player-piano' or 'pianola' as they were sometimes called. Twenty-five of these instruments were built as a test batch and proved to be of high musical quality. They had cast-iron frames, air motors and top-quality wooden bodies, which were to be the product's downfall. The Woodworkers Union refused to make the bodies on piece work, as had been their custom for airframes, and without that form of rigid costing, the project was not viable. Of the few that were sold, one happy purchaser was still using hers in 1969 and enquiring of the company where service could be obtained!

The government introduced a 47 hour working week to help solve the shortage of work generally but this did little to boost the economy. One pound

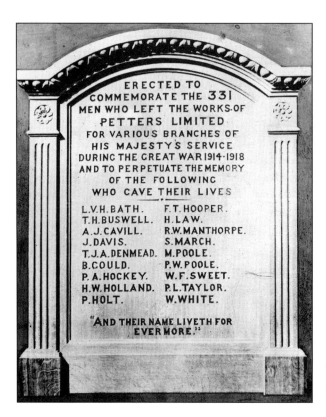

ERECTED TO
COMMEMORATE THE 331
MEN WHO LEFT THE WORKS·OF
PETTERS LIMITED·
FOR VARIOUS BRANCHES OF
HIS MAJESTY'S SERVICE
DURING THE GREAT WAR 1914·1918
AND TO PERPETUATE THE MEMORY
OF THE FOLLOWING
WHO GAVE THEIR LIVES

L.V.H.BATH.   F.T.HOOPER.
T.H.BUSWELL.   H.LAW.
A.J.CAVILL.   R.W.MANTHORPE.
J.DAVIS.   S.MARCH.
T.J.A.DENMEAD.   M.POOLE.
B.COULD.   P.W.POOLE.
P.A.HOCKEY.   W.F.SWEET.
H.W.HOLLAND.   P.L.TAYLOR.
P.HOLT.   W.WHITE.

"AND THEIR NAME LIVETH FOR
EVERMORE."

The plaque in Petters'
Westland factory commemora-
ting the fallen employees in
the First World War

and 10s notes were introduced and the sovereign coin phased out, while income tax rose to 6s in the pound.

The government also lifted the wartime ban on cross-country flying and was seen to actively support private flying clubs. Westland took this opportunity to sell a few civilian aircraft and in 1919 they announced the Limousine. The four-seat cabin biplane flew very well on tests, so much so that Robert Norton took his secretary, Miss Stansfield, complete with notebook and typewriter, for a publicity flight. Letters were dictated and typed while the flight was in progress, making it possibly the first 'air mail' service!

Following the Air Ministry's announcement of a competition to be held at Martlesham Heath in 1920, Westland hurriedly redesigned the Limousine as a six-seater for more commercial appeal. The aircraft won the Small Aeroplane class in the August competition but received only £7,500 instead of the £10,000 offered on the grounds that it did not reach expectations. This official explanation did more harm to sales than if it had not won. Capt. A.S. Keep, the test pilot, was busy throughout this period with the Limousine Four and then the Six, followed by the

A Petter 'S' type 18 hp surface ignition or semi-diesel marine oil engine, *c.* 1920

competition. He also carried out experimental work with a flying-wing design and found time to marry the managing director's daughter in between flights!

The flying-wing concept was given to Petters/Westland by the Air Ministry's Directorate of Technical Development. It followed a theory by the Russian inventor M. Wyevodsky that an aircraft would benefit if the wing aerofoil were merged with the fuselage, so eliminating external bracing and making an uninterrupted wingspan. The resultant very thick wing-root gave the 'Dreadnought' a futuristic appearance.

The Dreadnought prototype performed well on taxiing and short hops off the ground but stalled on its maiden flight, crashing on to the airfield from about 60 ft. Keep was severely injured, with his left leg being amputated below the knee; for some time it was thought he might also loose the right leg. After surgery lasting many months he returned to work, though he never piloted an aircraft again.

Aircraft production was quiet but the engine factory could not keep up with demand as sales recovered after the war. Half the aircraft factory changed to engine production and the old Nautilus works closed. Capt. Richard (Dick) Petter returned from his POW confinement to be sent to manage the newly opened Glasgow office.

About this time, Herbert Brookes designed a new ignition lamp that enabled oil engines to be started in a minute from cold instead of the normal 10 minutes. The innovation was rushed into production with a great deal of publicity as the competition had nothing to compare with that performance.

Robert J. Norton, Petter Westland commercial manager, *c.* 1920

The six seat Petter Westland Limousine executive aircraft and probably the first machine to produce 'air mail' from an on–board secretary and typewriter

Capt. A.S. Keep, Petter
Westland's first test pilot

The ill-fated Petter Westland Dreadnought, 1924

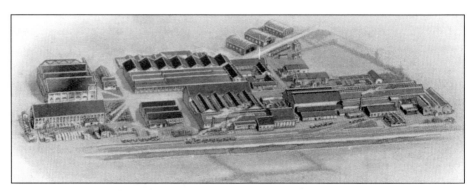

The Petter Westland works viewed from an aircraft in 1920

The Plough works started to manufacture agricultural equipment complete with Petter engines. One of these devices was a powered roller suitable for estates, golf courses, large lawns, paths and terraces. The 3 hp Petter Junior engine was mounted over two heavy rollers, each fitted with a compensating gear to assist turning in its own length, while the driver sat over a small articulated third roller. The machine was equipped with a reverse gear, a foot-brake and had sufficient power to climb a gradient of 1:10. Simplicity of operation was the keynote and its sales literature stated, 'Even a lad can drive it'. In fact, it could be left to drive itself, for with the aid of an optional extra the roller would prescribe a circular path, automatically being steered into an ever widening track. One satisfied owner wrote from his Hertfordshire estate: 'I write to let you know how pleased I am with the Petter Motor Roller. It has been working now for twelve months and has given me every satisfaction. It has proved thoroughly efficient and up to the present time has required no repairs. I have derived great advantage from its use on my roads and the lawns have been thoroughly well rolled. Moreover, the use of the roller has enabled me to dispense with the services of two of my garden labourers. I feel sure that if this roller becomes known to the agricultural and garden world, it will have great success.' Presumably the unemployment level would have risen accordingly!

Petters opened an office and showroom in Vancouver, with James H.B. Petter as manager. Harry had emigrated to Canada some years earlier. The new company was known as Canadian Petter and initially operated from the premises of B.C. Equipment on Howe Street, Vancouver.

Petters formed a partnership in April 1919 with Vickers under the name Vickers-Petters Ltd. This was to manufacture oil engines up to 500 hp and produce them at the old Rudolph Diesel factory in Ipswich. The factory had been designed for production of engines up to 1,000 hp per cylinder but after

A 1919 Petter Junior powered 'ride-on' roller with apprentice Jim Hallett in the driving seat

the owner's death Vickers bought the factory, in February 1913.

Vickers originally saw Ipswich as the ideal place to build their airless injection engines for submarines, but it was underused so the partnership with Petters seemed ideal. Petters' larger engines were primarily used for marine propulsion, electrical power generation and water pumping stations; they became firm favourites with shipbuilders, owners and skippers because of their reliability and economy. Many celebrities insisted on their latest marine acquisitions being powered by the engines, including the Duke of Westminster who specified two 220 hp propulsion engines and two 100 hp auxiliaries for his converted trading ship *Flying Cloud*. The engines gave his 863 ton, four-masted trader a cruising speed of 8½ knots, while the amenities provided by the auxiliary engines transformed the vessel into a luxury, long-distance cruising motor yacht.

The motor vessel *Karen*, powered by two 240 hp Petter engines, journeyed from her Essex berth to Gibraltar in four days and reported the bearings as staying cool all the way! The largest marine propulsion installation for Vickers-Petter was the Earl of Dunraven's *Sona*, a 169 ft motor yacht with two 500 hp engines giving a speed of 13¼ knots.

A Vickers-Petter heavy oil engine, *c.* 1920

The Duke of Westminster's 863 ton schooner *Flying Cloud* powered by two Vickers-Petter 220 hp oil engines and one 100 hp auxiliary

The Earl of Dunraven's MY *Sona*, a 554 ton, 169 ft vessel powered by two Vickers-Petter S6M, 510 hp at 250 r/min., oil engines providing a speed of over 13 knots

The ten sizes of marine engines made at the Ipswich factory ranged from a two-cylinder 50 hp model to the six cylinder of 510 hp. The company proudly boasted that once started, the engines would run indefinitely, providing the lubricator boxes were maintained, as no other maintenance was necessary.

The small engine division at Yeovil added a new unit to their impressive range in the form of the 'Little Pet', a 1½ hp oil engine; within two years the name was changed to 'Universal' and later still it was merged with the 'M' range. The boom period of engine sales experienced in the immediate postwar years was over, with the slump in sales continuing for two years until 1921. To counteract the downturn in sales, Petters took the bold step of reducing prices by 20 per cent, making the cost of a Junior just £20. The new sale price was about the same as the factory cost of producing it, but it kept production going and ultimately led to an all-time high in terms of sales. The Westland foundry found new customers for its ability to cast mild steel and low carbon crucible steel. They supplied castings of cylinder heads and crankcase blocks for London Buses, and similar parts for the 3-litre Bentley, Hotchkiss and Bull-Nose Morris cars.

Edwin P. Wrinch, an ex-Daimler man, was appointed works manager at

The Petter-Light
automatic electric lighting
set for domestic and
workshop use, *c.* 1922

Westland when production had never been more complicated, for there were
now twenty-one different engines being manufactured on the site.

Receiving radio broadcasts was taken for granted in many households,
although the spread of electricity to every town and hamlet was still far from
complete. The availability of portable lighting sets, like the Petter-Light or the
smaller Alpha-Petter set, brought wireless entertainment into the homes of many
people. The first wireless broadcast for the public was made in 1922 from
London's Savoy Hill radio station, known as 2LO. The convenience of the
Petter-Light set with its automatic start-up when a light switch was operated,
made this unit ideal for small houses and shops. The smaller Alpha-Light was
intended for bungalows or very small houses but could also be supplied with 'on
demand' automatic starting.

In 1923 Petters won a Royal Agricultural Society silver medal at the Newcastle
Show for another invention. This was a cold-starting device for any size of oil
engine and provided immediate running without pre-heating. A special charge in
a paper tube was placed into a metal holder and screwed into the cylinder head.
When ignited, the charge provided sufficient heat for the engine to run until

The 1923 Petter Patent cold-starter for 'S' type engines was awarded the RAS silver medal

normal operating temperatures were attained. Each engine was sold with 150 cold starters and replacements of a similar quantity could be purchased for 14s.

Ernest Petter turned his attentions to politics in January 1924, by standing unsuccessfully for parliament as an Imperial Preference and Fair Trade for British Industries candidate for North Bristol. In the same year, he became president of the British Engineers Association and was appointed as planning consultant for the Palace of Engineering at the British Empire Exhibition at Wembley. The company exhibited in the Palace of Engineering and organized a railway excursion for employees on 28 June 1924 at a cost of 12s 6d (63p) per head; over 450 made the journey. It is often said that during the 'slump' of the twenties, loyalty between workers and management died, but the magazine *British Home & Export Journal* commented favourably on a visit made to the Ipswich works of Vickers-Petters. It said, 'Good fellowship is the spirit of the place, the workers, managers and directors quite obviously having a thorough understanding with each other.'

CHAPTER SEVEN

1924–27
A Car for Africa

The crippling trade depression of the early twenties and increasing labour unrest made things gloomy for the remainder of the decade. The exception was that hardly a week went by without a new aviation record, or a land or water speed record being established. High altitude records were reached and it seemed there was nothing that aviators and speed kings would not attempt. Only Mount Everest remained unconquered, but not for long!

The 'garden village' development on the Westland site, abandoned at the outbreak of war, was resumed in mid-1924; fifty-eight houses were completed and occupied. The company, always keen to promote leisure activities for its workers, encouraged the formation of Yeovil and Petters Football Club, the Petter Works Band, and hockey, cricket and angling teams. An annual Westland Horticultural and Poultry Show was staged for the first time and held in the works canteen. In subsequent years, as the show grew in size, it moved outdoors on to the airfield.

A strange departure from manufacturing engines occurred in 1924, with the company selling VF cylinder oil. This commodity became good business for Petters as they acted as one of the largest oil distributors in the country as well as selling the lubricant to fourteen overseas countries. By 1939 the product was being sold as Shell VP Petter Oil.

A unique decision was made in 1925 when the company chose to re-introduce the Handyman oil engines. This was the first occasion on which an obsolete range had been revived. The relaunch was accompanied by a special publicity campaign targeted at farmers and pursued the line that winter weather was the ideal time when employees should be found work indoors creating supplies from raw material. It pointed out that with a Handyman, a labourer could produce gateposts, fencing, firewood, corn, root-pulp or pump water or generate electricity. The engines were offered at such a keen price it was suggested that it was cheaper to buy than have an existing one repaired.

Petters in Moscow, October 1923

Percy Petter was elected Mayor of Yeovil in 1926, a position he retained for two difficult years through the Coal and General strikes.

Only sixty of Petters' employees joined the General Strike, which showed remarkable loyalty to the company. Percy had been elected as a councillor in 1915 and continued to serve in that capacity for the next thirty years. He was also a Justice of the Peace and remained an active member of the Christian Brethren although he was an Anglican. In 1919, he took part in the Preachers' Walk from Bath to London.

Capt. Dick R.C. Petter returned to Yeovil from the London office in 1925 to become joint manager of the 12½ acre Westland works; later in the year he went on an extended world sales tour.

In April 1926 the coal miners went on indefinite strike for better pay and conditions. When the First World War finished in 1918, coal-producing technology had been exported to countries with mining potential and there followed a decline in coal demand from British pits, with an adverse effect on the country's balance of payments for many years. From the record coal production output of 287 million tons in 1913, it fell to 227 million tons in 1938 with exports falling from 98 million to 36 million tons.

A 1924 Petter Universal
paraffin or petrol engine

The Trades Union Council called a national strike on 3 May 1926 to add weight to the miners' dispute; 1,500,000 workers walked out of their employers' factories and offices and police with troops were called in to operate transport, generating stations, waterworks, sewage plants and other key industries. The TUC printed their own newspaper to keep their members informed of events while the HMSO printed the *British Gazette* written by Winston Churchill. Failure to clarify their strike demands by 12 May led the TUC to abandon the dispute as workers were beginning to drift back to employment. The failure of the strike lost the unions some 500,000 members who were disillusioned with organized labour.

Against this background of disruption, Petters embarked on yet another attempt to produce motor cars. For over a year the company had been studying the South African market where it was already well represented. Several sales tours were organized by Douglas Seaton, an engineer-representative and ex-apprentice.

Seaton's tours of African agents and customers were made difficult because of the rough terrain and poor roads. From his reports it was obvious a special

Seaton–Petter Colonial car, 1926

vehicle was needed to provide reliable transport and occasional sleeping accommodation. Percy Petter designed such a vehicle and a prototype was built as the Seaton-Petter Colonial car.

The newly formed British Dominion Car Co. was announced on 15 February 1926 to sell the car from showrooms in Berkeley Square, London, or the factory run by Douglas Seaton as managing director in Yeovil. The factory was the old Nautilus engine works at Reckleford where a demonstration was given to *Motor* magazine, which published a review on 23 February 1926. Marketed as a 10-18 hp car, it had several unique features, and sold for £125 in chassis form or £150 with a choice of four different bodies, including 7 cwt and 10 cwt vans; the price was later reduced to £100. The coachwork was detachable from the chassis in under 4 minutes to allow 'porterage' across rivers, etc., although, as tests showed, there was very little the car could not negotiate. The robust chassis was independent from the body and carried the running boards, mudguards, engine, transmission and axles.

The Herbert Sammonds-designed two-stroke engine of 1,319 cc was patented by Petters and made in the Westland factory. It comprised two water-cooled cylinders of 89 mm with a stroke of 106 mm giving extremely good low-speed torque. Combustion mixture was fed into the crankcase via

The chassis, engine and radiator of the 1926 Seaton-Petter Colonial car

steel induction plates, so making an engine with just five moving parts. The cylinder block was cast integral with the upper half of the crankcase and had two large inspection plates giving access to the big-end bearings. A single Cox carburettor fed petroil mixture through a 'Y' type inlet manifold to the spring-steel induction plates, these being actuated by internal air pressures created by piston movement. The rated output of the engine was reached at 1,600 r/min, although it could be revved easily to 2,500 r/min. The maximum speed was quoted as 64 km/hr (40 mph), with a fuel consumption of 30-32 mpg. The engine was planned to be replaced by a four-cylinder 15.6 hp version with the car boasting four-wheel hydraulic brakes and semi-elliptic springing front and rear, but this was never produced. The 10-18 hp car had quarter elliptic leaf springing mounted in the unusual configuration of two on the rear axle and one, centrally, on the front axle, providing cat-like agility. One-in-three gradients could be climbed with only an electric motor-like purr from the engine.

The brakes were of a curious design and similar in operation to the modern disc calliper, only they operated in the horizontal plane rather than the vertical. The 7 in shoes were positioned either side of the rim-type drums and mounted on the rear axle only; instant adjustment or lining replacement could be carried out and the effectiveness in stopping the car in all circumstances was most notable. Power from the engine was fed via a single-plate Borg and Beck clutch to a three speed and reverse gearbox then by open prop-shaft, with sealed oil-filled joints, to a Canadian-built rear axle. The 76 cm (30 in) × 9 cm (3½ in) artillery-type wheels gave good traction and ground clearance.

The fuel capacity and low consumption provided the car with a 200 mile range, and being equipped with excellent Rotax lighting the Colonial car made ideal transport for the traveller in South Africa. The two passengers could sleep full length in the rear with the tailgate either open or closed.

When demonstrating the car, Douglas Seaton would often ask prospective purchasers to sit in the rear while he negotiated an obstacle course in the yard of the old Nautilus engine works. The course consisted of building debris in the form of mounds of sticky clay 3–4 ft high, interspersed with large blocks of granite or masonry of about 300 mm (12 in) cube. The car, complete with its occupants, traversed these obstacles at 24–32 Rph (15 to 20 mph). While demonstrating the vehicle to *Motor* magazine, a front tyre burst and the vehicle rammed an iron fence, having been deflected from a mound of clay because of excessive speed. Seaton then selected reverse gear and accelerated fast before turning on full lock on another slope to finally scrape alongside a corrugated-iron shed. It was said 'that during the demonstration, no undue jolting was experienced nor was there any feeling of insecurity, despite the angle of the car at times'.

Under two hundred cars were built and sold, mostly to overseas customers, but difficulties were encountered with limited production line manufacturing and the setting up of servicing and spares agents. Within a few years the British Dominion Car Co. closed. Douglas Seaton stayed in the motor trade and became the proprietor of a Yeovil garage bearing his name. The garage building, designed by John Petter, was erected on the site of the original Petter foundry and redevelopment has since made it part of Tesco's car park.

In 1926, Petters managed to pay a 5 per cent dividend to shareholders, the first for six years. They also embarked on a vigorous sales campaign for their marine engines in the form of commissioning two boats, the *Annette* and the *April*, to work as floating demonstrations around the Thames estuary or cruising at a steady 8 knots off the south coast.

Another vessel to receive publicity was the MV *Yapura* operating on Lake Titicaca at 12,500 ft in the mountains of Peru. This 37.8 m (125 ft) 6.5 knot crude-oil tanker was powered by a Petter 100 hp marine engine and had an 8 hp auxiliary for electric lighting. The vessel and engines had to be transported in sections and components from the port of arrival across mountainous country to be assembled on the lakeshore. Similar publicity was given to engine sales to the royal estates of Balmoral and Sandringham, plus the purchase of an oil engine by the Grand Lama's monastery in Lhasa.

In the same year, Vickers-Petters announced the new 'C' type engine which represented an advanced design. This heavy oil two-stroke had double the

Sleeping arrangements in the Seaton-Petter Colonial car

compression ratio of the previous range, placing it between a semi-diesel and a full cold starting diesel. The compression ignition was assisted by a low voltage glow-plug giving the airless fuel injection the necessary combustion for easy starting; the engine also had 20 per cent better fuel consumption than engines of similar size.

Production at the Ipswich factory was never good and after the Iron-Moulders' strike of 1920, the situation declined. The partnership with Vickers ceased by mutual agreement on 8 December 1926, and Petters began work on another new range of engines to replace the 'C' type. Ernest moved from his London office to take charge of the Ipswich works, hoping to breathe renewed life into the factory now operating under the name of Petters (Ipswich) Ltd.

More experimental flying was undertaken by Petters' Westland division in 1926. In conjunction with Professor G.T.R. Hill, they were commissioned by the Air Ministry to work on another flying-wing project. After initial tests at the Royal Aircraft Establishment at Farnborough, the Hill-Westland Pterodactyl project moved to Yeovil. Several prototypes of these strange-looking machines were made and often thrilled crowds at London's annual air show at Hendon aerodrome.

Typical Petter sales brochure for the 'S' type engine, *c.* 1920s

Other air displays caught the company's attention and it was at one of these that another accident occurred. Maj. Lawrence Openshaw, chief test pilot for Westland, was killed while taking part in an air race at Bournemouth, just a few weeks after he married the eldest daughter of Robert Bruce on 12 April 1927. Unfortunately, Openshaw's Widgeon III collided with another competitor and both aircraft crashed, killing the pilots.

To increase sales during the depression the company introduced their first petrol engine, a modified 'M' type, in 1927. The reason for this departure from oil was that in some countries petrol was cheaper than paraffin. When taxation changed in 1928, a compression plate was offered, enabling owners to run the engine on the then cheaper paraffin oil.

Ben Jacobs, the original designer of the Petter engine thirty-three years earlier, made news in 1927 with yet another invention. He solved the problems of metered lubrication for stationary engines and unattended machinery with his Calibrater Sight Feed Mechanical Lubricator.

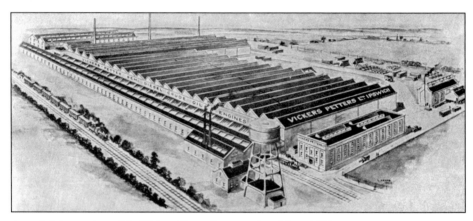

An artist's impression of the Vickers–Petter factory at Ipswich, *c.* 1920

The Petter calibrater
automatic oiling system
fitted to an 'S' type
engine, 1927

As engines and machines developed, their speed of operation increased, so the old method of drip-feed lubrication was insufficient to keep the bearings from seizing. Jacobs' invention continuously regulated the flow of oil to bearings or other wearing surfaces and only required the reservoir and its sight feed tube to be kept full of lubricant. Sixteen different lubrication points could be connected to the calibrater which was powered by any rotating shaft on the equipment it was safeguarding. The sixteen individual points could be adjusted by hand to suit the component, and thereafter the feed was maintained automatically. A priming handle was provided for extra lubricant during initial 'start-up' if required. The calibrater became standard equipment on all Petter engines from $1\frac{1}{2}$ hp to 400 hp up to 1939 and on some power units until 1950.

Petters decided to invest heavily in extending the Westland works as they felt the recession would not last long and wanted to be in a good position when volume orders returned. A heavy machine shop 100 m (330 ft) long and 32.7 m (108 ft) wide was erected to contain four 25.4 tonne overhead cranes; a new office block, an engine test shop and a larger power station were also constructed.

CHAPTER EIGHT

1927–31

The Atomic Age

The government was well aware of the serious economic situation as a result of continuous strikes, and concerned at the decline of the fledgling aircraft industry since the end of the war. To assist in the promotion of private flying, they made £20,000 available to the Air Ministry and charged them with the task of promoting ten private flying clubs around the country. Each club received a grant of £2,000 from the Air Ministry for the purchase of new aircarft, to be repaid over two years.

The Air Ministry also organized aero competitions at Lympne on the south coast to stimulate public interest in aircraft and flying. Petters Westland saw this as a good opportunity to promote their Wood Pigeon MkI and Widgeon MkII aircraft and entered them in the first competition. The smaller machine was badly damaged when it clipped a hillside as a result of severe down draught while negotiating a tight turn at low altitude in a valley. The Widgeon MkII, which sold for £750 complete with airworthy certifcate, went on to win its class.

By August 1927 it was clear that economies were needed at Petters' Ipswich factory. Subsequent financial reviews indicated considerable savings would be achieved if all production moved to Yeovil and this was implemented. The move was made all the more attractive for a new engine testshop had been constructed at the Westland works and was equipped for internal combustion engines up to 500 hp.

The Ipswich factory was closed and put up for sale but there were few enquiries as heavy industry was very much in decline. An American printing machine manufacturer was about to purchase in 1929 when the US financial crisis stopped the deal; it was still for sale in 1933, by which time Petters had lost over £250,000 on the venture, which almost ruined them. Petters moved their London office from Queen Victoria Street, where they had been since 1899, to Terminal House, Grosvenor Gardens. A feeling of restlessness existed throughout the country and affected everyone. Guy Petter resigned his post as resident director at Ipswich and returned to Yeovil to concentrate on his adding machine

The London office of Petters
Ltd, *c.* 1922, situated at 73b
Queen Victoria Street, EC4

Petter portable air compressor, *c.* 1927

The New Zealand Government's *Maui Pomare* powered by two Petter 'C' type engines developing 1,200 hp and providing a speed of 11.75 knots, 1928

invention. Capt. Dick Petter returned from Glasgow to become a director of Petters Ltd and took over from Ernest in London, so allowing him to concentrate on his political future.

On 12 February 1925, Ernest Waddams Petter became a Knight Bachelor. He received his knighthood from King George V at Buckingham Palace for his consultancy planning work in respect of the British Empire Exhibition at Wembley. The knighthood recognition of Ernest's contribution to engineering and the growth of the family business confirms the truth in a verse by Emerson. This was often used as a slogan by the company in their early sales literature and has been adapted, with apologies by the author, as a title for this biography of the Petter family and their business activities.

> If a man can write a better book,
> Preach a better sermon,
> Or make a better mousetrap than his neighbour,
> Though he build his house in the woods,
> The world will make a beaten track to his door.

The company enjoyed a good standing in Yeovil, so when agreement was sought from the Great Western Railway to erect special signs on the platform of

The Westland Wapiti, 1927

Yeovil Junction, this was readily agreed. The large signs announced, 'Change here for Yeovil, Home of Petter Oil Engines and Westland Aircraft'.

To boost flagging sales, prices were cut and a store built to house one thousand engines to meet the expected demand. Air compressors of 175 cfm at 100 psi and powered by 42 hp Petter engines were added to the range of products. Percy whipped his employees into renewed vigour with countless utterances along the lines of, 'Work is the core of life whose influence stretches into the lives of employees, representatives and agents, all users of every colour and creed from the Arctic to the Antarctic'.

Obviously, these calls for greater effort were effective. Production and sales increased and the Yeovil & Petter United Football Club reached the qualifying rounds of the 1928 FA Cup. The team, with ten full-time Petter employees, was only beaten by Plymouth Argyle. They had come a long way since 1922 when they first qualified for the Southern League, followed by the championship of the Western Division in 1923 and winning 3–2 against Bournemouth & Boscombe in the English League.

As the National Grid system spread throughout Britain distributing electrical power, the sales of small engines for lighting sets gradually diminished. Now it was the turn of Petters' Westland Aircraft division to come to the aid of the company's flagging profits. They won an Air Ministry competition with their recently designed Wapiti aircraft and so gained a contract for twenty of the biplanes. The first machine was delivered to HRH The Prince of Wales, who was a keen pilot. Within three years, orders for

An Atomic powered saw-bench purchased by Sir Cosmo Antrobus, 5th Baronet, at Amesbury Abbey in 1920 still producing 20 tons of logs per day in 1969 for 2.2 litre of fuel

five hundred Wapitis had been received from air forces around the world. The Wapiti was the first all-metal aircraft to enter military service; eventually, one thousand were constructed at Yeovil and in South Africa under licence, including a diesel-powered special that attained 28,000 ft, a world height record for a diesel-powered aircraft.

When the Wall Street stock market crashed in New York it created further trading difficulties in Europe. Petters were faced with the prospect of having nothing to replace the phased-out 'C' type engine. The labour force of over two thousand had to be kept in work and orders were still fluctuating. The company decided in January 1929 to press ahead with the development of a new type of oil engine. Their Atomic range was launched and although an instant success, did not prevent redundancies. Seventy-eight valued employees had to be laid off in 1930; the first redundancies in over thirty years of manufacturing.

Initially, the Atomic cold-starting diesel engines ranged from 25 to 65 hp in one- to four-cylinder specification. These heavy, high compression, airless injection engines operated on the two-stroke cycle. They were relatively low speed and possessed a large bore and stroke, making them ideal for applications where weight was not a disadvantage and a hard working life was expected. Within four years, the 5 to 20 hp versions were available; these could be hand-started without heating or cartridges. A six-cylinder model was also added to the range, taking it to 480 hp. The Atomics operated at a high level of efficiency, about 80 per cent, as they had a built-in scavenge system which made the top of the range ideally suited for electrical power generation. Typical applications were Canadian and South American mining companies, stone-crushing plants and water treatment works.

By 1931 the slump in trade was causing concern for there were some 3,000,000 office and factory workers unemployed in Britain and the fishing industry was showing signs of collapse. Sir Ernest turned to politics for the third time in his life to oppose the Baldwin nominee Duff Cooper, later Lord Norwich, in the St George's, Westminster, constituency.

Sir Ernest's forthright policy and views on unemployment were those of Lord Beaverbrook – 'empire free trade and duties on foreign imports' – a solution to the nation's difficulties that he maintained was the only means to renewed industrial prosperity. He fought a very good campaign according to *The Times* newspaper and only lost by a small majority. Shortly after this unsuccessful attempt to become an MP, he was made vice-president of the Institution of Mechanical Engineers and became a founder member of the Society of British Aircraft Constructors and an executive member of the Federation of British Industries.

A 1929 Petter Atomic single-cylinder oil engine

Capt. Dick Petter returned from an extended world sales tour to rejoin the company as assistant managing director. Having seen the way in which business was being conducted overseas, he produced a credit scheme to assist British manufacturers with their export difficulties. Apparently, Germany had introduced an easy payment system for their export customers; however, when Petters' scheme was submitted to the Board of Trade, there was no reaction and the idea was not pursued.

There was a brighter side to the early thirties: England won the Schneider Trophy outright. The Supermarine S6b seaplane won the 1931 race breaking the speed record at 340.08 mph; having won the race three years out of five, England retained the trophy.

Malcolm Campbell set a new land speed record on the sands of Daytona Beach, USA, with a 246 mph drive in Bluebird, while Kay Don established a new water speed record of 103.49 mph. The railways were not forgotten for the Cheltenham Flyer became the fastest train in the world with a speed of 78 mph. The following year, Campbell raised the land speed record to 253.96 mph; Kay

Percy Petter's gramophone record made in 1934 to promote two-stroke engines against four-stroke designs

Don improved on his water speed to 119.8 mph on the waters of Loch Lomond while a Great Western Railway train clocked 81 mph on the run from Swindon to London.

The search for sales further afield led to the Petter Westland division exhibiting a Wapiti at the Buenos Aires Air Show in 1931 along with an 'S' type oil engine. Percy Petter, always vocal in his views, committed his voice to disc the following year to promote the advantages of two-stroke engines over those of the four-stroke cycle. The little 4 in fibre disc, made by Durium Products of Slough, is in the author's collection of Petter memorabilia.

CHAPTER NINE

1931–37

The End of the Beginning

The early thirties saw a concentrated effort on exports of engines so the sales literature was printed in twenty languages. Percy Petter, always the writer, put pen to paper to produce *The Psychology of Trade Depression*, the contents of which sound strangely familiar in 1995. The article suggested, 'Psychology, or the state of mind, has much to do with chronic alternations of boom and slump. When people get nervous the result is a check on all forms of enterprise. Merchants and shopkeepers let their stocks run down, manufacturers are starved of orders, workers are laid off, consumption is reduced, so the vicious circle goes on. But goodwill is necessary between employer and employee, between nation and nation. We need patience, courage, faith, industry and understanding of the fellow point of view'.

In 1931, Britain came off the Gold Standard and the financial collapse of the pound sterling soon followed. H.S. Aspinall resigned from Petters' London office to become engineering general manager at English Electric.

Guy Petter spent considerable time behind closed doors developing his adding machine, while Sir Ernest's son, Willoughby, or Teddy as he was known, joined the company having graduated from Cambridge with exceptionally high honours. He achieved a first with a mechanical sciences tripos and shared the aeronautical prize with another student. Teddy started work in the engine assembly shop, moving to the aircraft drawing office where he stayed for two years before becoming an assistant to Robert Bruce.

The success of the Atomic diesels led Petters into another development aimed at the automotive and traction market, a field that had eluded them for so many years. They produced the ACE Atomic engines in early 1932; these had no relationship to the existing Atomic range and were high compression ignition,

W.E.W. (Teddy) Petter on leaving
Cambridge University with a first in
Mechanical Sciences Tripos and a shared
aviation award, 1927

two-stroke motors. To avoid confusion with the larger more established
Atomics, the new engines were later marketed as High Compression Ignition
Engines. One of their features was the individual air scavengers to each cylinder
which they exceeded in cubic capacity. They were water-cooled power units
built in three- and four-cylinder configuration only and operated at 250 to
1,600 r/min, with the optimum power at 1,000 r/min.

A lorry powered by a three-cylinder version was used as a mobile testbed and
had good acceleration with a marked absence of the typical diesel knock. A
similar size engine was installed in a shunting locomotive operating in Petters'
railway sidings on the Westland site. The tests proved the three-cylinder engine
was suitable for 4 ton lorries while the four cylinder could power road vehicles
of up to 6 tons. The tests also showed considerable fuel savings over steam- or
petrol-powered locos in the shunting application.

The High Compression engines were also sold with electrical generating-sets;
the 30 hp three cylinder producing 18 kW at 1,000 r/min, while the four-
cylinder model was adapted for marine use to produce 40 hp at a similar engine

A Petter 6-cylinder 400 hp Atomic cold-starting diesel, 1929

speed. Typical applications for the marine version were broad-beam barges and coastal fishing vessels.

In developing the High Compression engines, extensive use was made of Alpax aluminium, hence the weight of only 1,300 lb (610 kg) for the three-cylinder engine. However, the ACE project was not a success and they were withdrawn after a short period, while the original Atomics continued for some years.

Once more the name 'Universal' was used for a new small engine. Later changed to the PU series, this power unit was totally different to the 'M' type Universal. The new engine was an air-cooled, high-speed petrol engine of four-stroke design. The PU had a cylinder capacity of 2 hp and was available in single horizontal or twin opposed specification, making it extremely compact. To test the air-cooling, the prototype was run for an hour on full load in a core-oven within the Petter foundry at 140° F. The Oxford University Arctic Expedition of 1936 telegrammed news of a 2 hp version also performing well in sub-zero conditions north-east of Spitzbergen. A 1 ton factory truck powered by a PU sold well until the series ceased production in 1948. The engine was cheap to make and sold for £22 in single-cylinder form or £33 as a twin, with drive being available at full or half engine speed.

The 8 hp marine version of the PU8 was well suited for small inshore boats as

2   PETTER'S MONTHLY NEWS

The New High Speed Atomic Diesel Engine

FOR LOCOMOTIVES, ROAD VEHICLES, PORTABLE AIR COMPRESSORS, ELECTRIC GENERATING PLANTS, &c.

It gives us much pleasure to publish some particulars of the New High Speed Atomic Diesel Engine which has been the subject of extensive research work for the past two years.

Owing to the very gratifying results obtained from our Slow Speed Atomic Diesel Engines in service, it was evident to us when considering the design of this engine, that the best type of engine for the high speed series would be of the two-stroke cycle and the results which have been consistently obtained have more than justified this decision.

In order to ensure perfect combustion, when working at high speeds, the engine is fitted with independent air pumps for the scavenge air. These air pumps are driven from a separate crankshaft which is chain driven from the main crankshaft. With this arrangement it is possible to time the movement of the air pumps in relation to the opening of the ports by the main piston to the best advantage, and as the pressure of the scavenge air is not more than 2 lbs. per square inch is a negligible amount of power is required to drive them. This design also enables the crankcase of the engine to conform with the best accepted practice for high speed engines, incorporating a high pressure forced feed lubrication system for all bearings and a dry sump.

The greatest possible care has been taken in the general design of the engine in order to obtain the maximum power for weight of material without sacrificing reliability and durability. The absence of valves and valve gear in this type of engine is of tremendous importance. In the case of engines working on the four-stroke cycle, it is always difficult when running at these high speeds to ensure that all the valves are kept in perfect condition. If only one valve on a multi-cylinder engine does not function satisfactorily then the load is not equally shared on all the cylinders. The cylinder heads are of very simple design with no intricate water passages, etc., and are made of steel. Owing to the special shape of the combustion chamber, instant cold starting on fuel oil is obtained without resource to any pre-heating device or hot spot of any kind, either by hand starting or from an electric motor.

The sectional drawing on page 3 shows the main construction of the engine. We intend to build these

Fig. 1. General Illustration of 3 Cylinder Engine.

engines in 2, 3 and 4 cylinders, the main cylinders having a bore of 4¼ in. by 5¼ in. stroke.

Owing to the use of independent scavenge pumps and the introduction of a high pressure lubricating oil system, the consumption of lubricating oil is negligible. Runs as long as 100 hours have been made without any noticeable drop in the level of the lubricating oil in the container. The fuel oil consumption is about .45 pints per B.H.P. per hour.

One very pleasing feature of the engine is its clean exhaust. Owing to the use of the independent scavenge pumps it is possible to have a small exhaust system with exhaust silencers similar to those in use on four-stroke cycle engines, thus obtaining the necessary degree of silence without causing a reduction in the power of the engine through back pressure. It will be evident from the above that as the engine has all the advantages of the four-stroke cycle type and none of its disadvantages, it is much superior in every way. Moreover, with these advantages an engine of the High Speed Diesel type can be placed in the hands of unskilled labour with every assurance that it will give satisfaction with the lowest possible maintenance charges.

The speed range for locomotive and road vehicle requirements is from 250 r.p.m. to 1,000 r.p.m., whilst for other purposes where the engine is required to run more or less at constant

Fig. 2. Shefflex Six-Wheel Lorry with High Speed Atomic Diesel Engine.

The 1937 Petter ACE Atomic automotive/traction power unit

The train test bed for the ACE engine

The 1 ton Petter auto-truck powered by their PU8 petrol engine and probably the last application made by the company, 1936

it was able to go from full ahead to full astern in 4 seconds. In the years to follow, PU8s were used to drive small air compressors mounted on two-wheel trolleys for starting the engines of Hurricane and Spitfire aircraft during the Battle of Britain.

In 1944, PU8-powered pontoons were used to ferry troops and tanks across the Rhine as the allied forces advanced through Germany. Men of the Royal Engineers manned the pontoons and steered the two PU8s mounted on opposite corners of the pontoons by manually moving the flexible shaft-driven propellers through 180 degrees.

The other engines being produced by Petters in 1936 included the 'M' series from $1\frac{1}{2}$ hp to 6 hp; semi-diesels of 6 hp to 21 hp; the Atomic cold-start series of 5 hp to 480 hp, and a range of electrical generating sets from 0.75 kW. Sales were not particularly good for industrial engines but the aviation side started to pick up, and this seesaw of fortunes alternated throughout the thirties.

The Wapiti aircraft had been the salvation of the aero division of Petters in 1927; it now became the workhorse of the Royal Air Force, seeing extensive service on the north-west frontier of India, and was the mainstay for the RAF auxiliary squadrons at home. The aircraft were also made under licence in South Africa where that country's air force standardized on the machine, as did the Chinese Air Force. The smallest air force of four Wapiti was operated by the King of Hadjaz.

The Petter TX1 Atomic – the last vintage engine, manufactured 30 June 1936, purchased and restored by apprentices in 1973 for the company museum

In 1931, two new aircraft designs were developed, the PV3 and PV6. The latter became the Wallace and went into production in 1933 to supersede the Wapiti in the Royal Air Force. The PV3 had started life as a private venture by Petters' Westland division which was hoping to produce a high-performance plane for army co-operation work, with possible later conversion to a carrier-based torpedo bomber.

The test flights of the PV3 attracted the interest of the Houston Mount Everest Expedition who were looking for a plane capable of being the first to fly over Mount Everest. Subject to alterations, the PV3 was ideal for the purpose; a supercharged Bristol Pegasus S3 engine was fitted and the rear cockpit enclosed. Further test flights to prove the modifications achieved 35,000 ft, which was higher than the mountain, so similar conversions were carried out on a Wallace.

Both planes were dismantled and shipped to Karachi where they were re-assembled and flown to the expedition base camp at Purnea. The expedition was funded by Lady Houston and led by Air Commodore P.F.M. Fellows, DSO, and controlled by the Chief Observer, Lt. Col. L.V.S. Blacker, OBE.

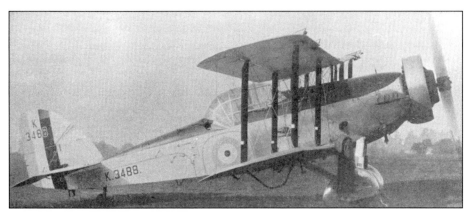

The Petter Westland Wallace, one of the first aircraft to overfly Everest, 1933

On the morning of 3 April 1933, the Wallace in the hands of Fl. Lt. J. McIntyre and with S.R. Bonnett, a photographer from Gaumont British Film Corporation on board, took off from Purnea for the 150 mile flight to Everest. The Wallace was accompanied by Lord Clydesdale and Col. Blacker as observer, in the Houston-Westland as the PV3 had been renamed. The planes flew in heavy mist for most of the time until at 19,000 ft they broke cloud to see Everest ahead. After more arduous climbing in the extreme cold they cleared the summit and returned to base, having been airborne for three and half hours.

A further flight was made on 19 April, when photographs and film were taken to thrill audiences and readers around the world. The Houston-Westland returned to Yeovil to continue research work as a flying testbed for the Bristol Aeroplane Co. The Wallace was re-equipped to military specification and delivered into squadron service with the Royal Air Force; it was the first aircraft to enter military service with enclosed front and rear cockpits under one canopy. The Wallace remained in the RAF for some time; in fact, there were still some being used for target-towing in the early part of the Second World War!

The company's chief test pilot, Harald J. Penrose, who had done much of the high-altitude work with the Houston-Westland project, had a narrow escape when testing the PV7, a high-wing, two-seat monoplane and forerunner of the Lysander. Penrose was over the Air Ministry's test airfield at Martlesham Heath carrying out test dives when a wing strut broke causing the wing to tear away from the fuselage. Luckily, the pilot was able to jump from a small window and parachute to safety, so becoming one of the first pilots to escape from a totally enclosed military aircraft; the parachute escape earned him membership of the Caterpillar Club.

The Houston-Westland PV3 making the first flight over Everest, 1933

During 1934, Sir Ernest's first wife, Angela Emma, daughter of Henry Petter of Calcutta, died. They had married in 1907 and had three sons and a daughter. The following year, Sir Ernest married Lucy Ellen, daughter of Charles Hopkins of Portsmouth.

In the early thirties Nissen-Petren Ltd was formed, with Ernest Petter as chairman and John, his younger architect brother, as managing director. John and his partner Percy Warren designed and built several Nissen-Petren barrel-roofed houses around Yeovil and the design was adopted for the ubiquitous wartime Nissen hut.

For many years Petters championed the two-stroke concept against the four-stroke design. Their arguments were at first accepted, but now they were being questioned by some of the foremost consulting engineers of the day. Percy Jackson, Petters' chief designer, was given the task of overcoming the problem, so in true Petter fashion, he compromised by producing the Blower Scavenge engine in the spring of 1935.

The Blower Scavenge engine had inlet ports with piston valves operated by the camshaft, which meant it could be converted to a four-stroke engine by changing the cylinder head. Within three years it was replaced by the Superscavenge engine designed by H.O. Farmer and subsequently Charles Dale; that engine was a two-stroke with patented arrangement of twin exhaust valves in the head. A series of patents resulted and the work progressed in conjunction

A typical Nissen-Petren 'barrel' house built near Yeovil, *c.* 1936

with the Armstrong Whitworth company under the name of the Kadenacy project. The engines were built in two- to six-cylinder specification, developing 125 to 375 hp with complete combustion and an invisible exhaust. The cylinder heads of these cast-iron engines provided special interest as they were water-cooled and housed a number of components.

The components were a copper-sheathed atomizer, two exhaust valves and a decompressor valve, all in very close proximity to one another. The Superscavenge engines were compact and automotive in appearance, although they were classed as low speed power units as they operated at a fixed 500 r/min.

A considerable amount of research and development was also in progress, including refinement of the Atomic range. As a result of research, the Harmonic Induction Engine appeared in 1936. This strange-looking single-cylinder, water-cooled two-stroke was a direct development of the Kadenacy project, standing column-like in appearance with a height of 109 cm (43 in) with radius corners and a flat top to the cylinder head. Only the small exterior flywheel and short drive-shaft broke the clean lines of this 16 hp, 1,000 r/min engine. Its method of operation is perhaps best described by quoting the sales brochure:

Whereas most diesel engines operating on the two-stroke principle require a supply of scavenged air, provided either by an independent scavenge blower or

The 1939 Petter Superscavenge 250 hp engine in the power station of a wallpaper works

produced as a result of crankcase compression, an entirely new and highly efficient principle has been employed.

As the name implies, the new principle incorporates the use of vibrations set up in the exhaust system, which not only ensure perfect scavenging, but result in the cylinder being filled with cool, clean air. A push-rod operated valve opens when the piston is nearing the end of its stroke and the burnt gases rush out of the cylinder. This sudden exodus of gases sets up pressure in the exhaust system that is much higher than the atmosphere. When the gases reach the atmosphere, the high pressure is dissipated resulting in a sudden fall in exhaust system pressure. A sudden and partial vacuum is thus created and communicated back to the cylinder, where the inlet ports are synchronised to open at this point, allowing swirling, cool, clean air to be drawn into the cylinder so providing efficient scavenging.

Although about one hundred Harmonics were made, the engine was far ahead of its time and was discontinued after about two years. A Harmonic was

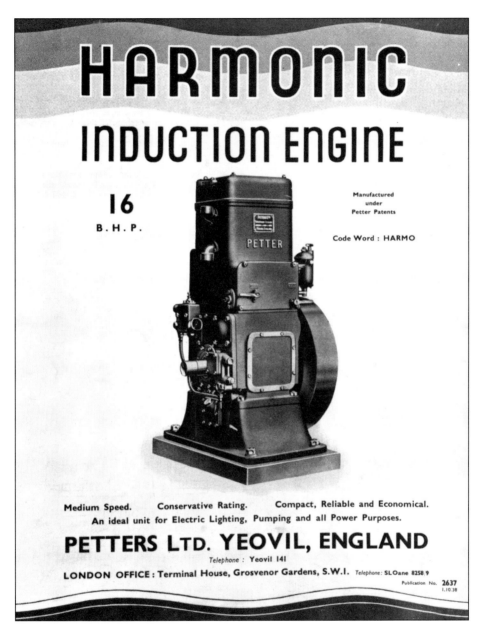

The 16 hp Petter Harmonic Induction engine, 1939

Herbert Sammonds, Petters' chief
engineer in the twenties and early
thirties before becoming managing
director of D. Napier & Son Ltd

presented to Loughborough College for R&D work to be carried out and was
still in laboratory use in 1964.

Herbert Sammonds, Petters' chief engineer, resigned in 1934 to join
Armstrong Whitworth in Newcastle. Sammonds' departure was a great loss to
the company for he had fifteen years knowledge and experience and took with
him Bert Cornish, a development engineer specializing in new designs.
Sammonds became general manager of Armstrong's R&D department and so
continued the liaison between Petters and Armstrong concerning the Kadenacy
and Harmonic projects. It was Sammonds who arranged for a Harmonic to be
sent to the Internal Combustion Research Association in Slough where it
proved invaluable in their work. Eventually, Sammonds moved to D. Napier &
Son of Acton, London, where he became managing director and received a
CBE before retiring in 1960.

The research work carried out by Petters kinetic diesel engine design was well
known and led to their being commissioned to produce a 160 hp engine for the

polar survey ship *Discovery II,* a research vessel destined to carry out survey work near the magnetic pole. The ship had to be virtually non-magnetic in construction, fittings and cargo so the Petter engine was constructed of special alloys for the wearing or load-bearing parts, while extensive use was made of bronze for the non-wearing components. Unfortunately, work on this unusual project had to be abandoned in 1939 with the outbreak of the Second World War.

CHAPTER TEN

1937–38
As One Door Closes . . .

Following disagreement with the chairman's wish to appoint his son, Teddy Petter, as technical director of the aviation branch, Robert A. Bruce retired as managing director in 1934 although he stayed as a consultant for a further three years. He died on 8 January 1948, aged seventy-nine. Sir Ernest took over as chairman and managing director, with Capt. Keep as general manager and W.E.W. (Teddy) Petter as technical director.

Teddy Petter produced his first aeronautical design to a specification from the Air Ministry for an army co-operation aircraft. This unique plane was the culmination of all Westland's work on high-wing monoplanes and ultimately became the Lysander. When the Lysander went into service with the RAF, it was the first aircraft to have fully slotted and flapped wings, so that despite a

The 1934-designed Westland Lysander, brainchild of W.E.W. Petter and used by the RAF in the Second World War in covert operations, army co-operation and air-sea rescue

The Petter Westland Pterodactyl Mk I tailless aircraft, the first of many prototypes built in the early twenties and thirties

heavy wing loading, it could take off and land easily on a football pitch. With that ability, the aircraft carried out over four hundred covert operations behind enemy lines at night for the landing or recovery of special agents and VIP refugees.

So good was the aircraft's slow-speed handling, it could be throttled back and trimmed to perform a perfect 'no-hands' three-point landing. By the outbreak of the Second World War, there were four squadrons of Lysanders in service carrying out parachute drops, ground attack, target and glider towing, air-sea rescue and night fighter operations. The aircraft was slow by comparision with other machines of the day, with a top speed of 237 mph, but nothing could out-fly its stalling point of 65 mph.

Further experimental work was carried out on the F7/30, a high-speed biplane designed to meet the Air Ministry's quest for a powerful single-seat fighter with short-landing ability. The F7/30 was one of the first aircraft to have a multi-gun installation in the fuselage firing through a synchronized airscrew.

Tailless flight was still being pursued by Capt. Hill with test pilot Penrose and the Mark V Pterodactyl. Equipped with a conventional prop instead of a 'pusher', this two-seat aircraft was of interest to the Air Ministry so was equipped with two synchronized Vickers guns firing forward through the propeller and a power-operated gun turret at the rear with an unequalled field of fire.

One of two prototype Westland Autogyros or rotating wing aircraft made in the thirties

Another strange aircraft to fly from Westland's Yeovil airfield was a result of combined design work with the Cierva Co. Known as the CL.20 Autogyro, this rotating-wing aircraft carried two passengers at a top speed of 106 mph produced from its Pobjoy 90 hp air-cooled engine. The rotor angle could be controlled directly from the pilot's seat instead of the conventional fixed-plane rotation of earlier autogiros. This was the start of development work culminating many years later in Westland becoming a major manufacturer of helicopter aircraft.

The aircraft division of Petters had become large and heavily involved in aeronautical research to Air Ministry specifications, and therefore it was decided the division should progress to individual status. On 4 July 1935, Petters announced the formation of Westland Aircraft Ltd, with a capital of £250,000 and a float of 500,000 5s shares on offer at 7s which were quickly over-subscribed.

The new board of Westland Aircraft Ltd comprised Sir Ernest Petter as chairman and joint managing director with Capt. Peter Acland; W.E.W (Teddy) Petter, technical director; John Fearn, director and works superintendent; and Air Vice Marshal N.D.K. MacEwen.

Westland opened their head office at Bush House in London's Strand area, where Petters joined them as they still retained a 50 per cent shareholding in the new company. A new wing assembly shop was built at Yeovil with 16,000 sq. ft of air-conditioned floor space.

The government were becoming increasingly concerned at political upheaval in Europe, with Germany once again giving cause for reappraisal of Britain's defences. Many Air Ministry specifications were issued and Westland were always very quick to respond with designs for many fine planes – all with a

The Westland Whirlwind designed by W.E.W. Petter, one of the last aircraft he designed before joining English Electric

distinct family likeness. However, there was one design that came off the drawing boards in 1936 looking like no other aircraft, the prototype of which was built and flew for the first time in 1938. Its performance quickly earned it the factory nickname of 'Crikey', and so was born the Westland Whirlwind with twin 885 hp vee-type Rolls-Royce Peregrine engines and an armament of four Hispano canons mounted in the nose; this was indeed a fighter aircraft. A later version named the Whirlibomber was the last aircraft to be designed by the Petter/Westland combination.

In 1936, Lt. Col. J.T.C. Moore-Brabazon, holder of the first British flying licence (dated 8 March 1910) and later to become Lord Brabazon of Tara, was appointed to the Petter board.

Hardly a month went past in this period without a change of some sort taking place or the passing on of an old employee. Ben Jacobs, Petters' first engine designer, died in 1937 aged seventy-seven, so ending a career with the company that started in 1893. He had given Petters their first oil engine and horseless carriage in 1895 and assisted in their various automotive quests in later years, and had invented the calibrater automatic lubricator that had given so much to the company in terms of added reliability.

Guy Petter resigned his directorship in 1936, having perfected his Rapid-Plus adding machine and seen it into limited production within the Westland works. One of the early production models was purchased from a Yeovil antique shop in 1966 and added to the company's museum stock. Guy sold the patent to the Bell Punch Co. Ltd, of Uxbridge, Middlesex, who produced the Sumlock range of specialist office calculating and ticket machines. He moved to Uxbridge,

The Rapid-Plus Petometer designed and initially made by Guy Petter at the Westland factory before it was sold to the Bell Punch Co., 1936

Alan P. Good

Chairman of A.B.E. Ltd., Chairman
of A.B.O.E. Ltd., Deputy Chairman and
Managing Director of Brush Electrical
Engineering Company Limited.

Alan Paul Good, Financier and Chairman
of Associated British Oil Engines, 1937

taking with him the apprentice who had been with the project throughout its development at Ipswich and Yeovil. The Rapid-Plus became part of the Sumlock range and the author met the apprentice in the late sixties. He was still at the Bell Punch as office manager and about to retire. Guy Petter died in 1948.

The final and probably the most significant change also came in 1937 with the announcement of Sir Ernest and Percy's retirement. Following board defeat for the suggestion of a merger with British Marine Aircraft and all the major changes taking place in the company they had established, they no longer considered they had anything to contribute to the 'progress'. Their retirement marked the end of an era that had lasted nearly fifty years.

The twins had given the world a name synonymous with quality, reliability and durability; they had given their country the means to defend itself and in so doing had provided many thousands of employees with something more than a wage packet; they had given pride and a sense of loyalty to the marque.

Alan Paul Good, a solicitor and management consultant specializing in commercial structuring and share dealing, headed a small group of investors who obtained a controlling interest in Petters Ltd by amassing shares. Born in Ireland in 1906, he had considerable charm, commercial ability and a massive presence as he weighed nearly 20 stone and stood almost 6 ft 6 in. When he became chairman of Petters Ltd, Moore-Brabazon retired and T.B. Keep became managing director. Capt. Petter and R.J. Norton remained as directors. Tommy Keep was an ex-director of Rootes and managing director of Commer & Karrier Motors, but no relation to Capt. Keep the test pilot. Three of the directors formed a works committee with their names giving the message 'Keep-Norton-Good', their task being to oversee all departments, to reduce overheads and production costs. One of their early directives was to cease the practice of making engines to customers' specifications, replacing them with standard engines.

Good initiated close liaison between other British oil engine manufacturers and suggested the exchange of directors. Charles Day of Mirrlees, Bickerton and Day joined the Petter board, while Good and Keep became directors of Mirrlees. Capt. Dick Petter and four other Petter directors joined the Brush

A relic of the Spanish Civil War, 1938. A bullet-holed Petter Atomic engine name plate; apparently the damage did not affect the engine's operation

Electrical Engineering board. Later, Good became chairman of Mirrlees. Tommy Keep spent considerable time in the Brush works in Loughborough as part of this elaborate stage management of liaison, while Good slowly gained control of each company. The Petter labour force had been unaware of the behind-the-scenes deals, for even Good's AGM speech to shareholders in October 1937 only made note of the reduced overheads achieved since the management change. The speech did hint at closer liaison with other oil engine companies but in fact Good was acquiring controlling interest in Brush Electrical Engineering, with the aim of merging Petters with Brush. In 1938, the labour force suddenly received notice that Petters' engine business was being transferred to Loughborough. The man charged with the intricate commercial dealings was Percy Sharp, secretary of Petters Ltd from 1935 to 1939, later to become director and secretary of the Brush Group, and finally director and secretary of Hawker Siddeley International in 1957. He managed to gain Petters' agreement to change their name to Associated British Engineering Ltd on 1 January 1939. The following day, ABE formed a new company, Petters Ltd, which was merged with Brush Electrical Engineering Co. In that way, Brush acquired the engine business of Petters, together with all the patents, etc., without purchasing the company.

ABE sold the greater part of Westland shares and the aerodrome site with its buildings and equipment to John Brown Ltd in July 1938; the remaining Petter shares in Westland were sold to Associated Electrical Industries. Having sold the Westland property, ABE were in the unusual position of having accrued considerable capital with no manufacturing or overhead liabilities.

CHAPTER ELEVEN

1938–45

. . . Another Opens

Much of the money acquired by ABE through the sale of Westland and the site was used to purchase shares in other engineering companies, for the phoney war had already begun and there was every prospect of considerable money to be made in the manufacture of munitions by such companies.

In 1938, Petters received a very large order from the Air Ministry for PU8s, the engines being destined for powering ground equipment on airfields. In the same year, the new 'A' series of air-cooled, four-stroke petrol engines of 1½ and 3 hp were launched. The 'A' series had the option of being paraffin fuelled and were aimed at agricultural applications; they were made for eight years before being superseded by the series II. These small, compact engines found favour with the Ministry of Defence and, like the PU8s, were purchased in large numbers for powering military ground equipment.

Petters' move from their birthplace in Yeovil started in January 1939; special freight trains and fleets of heavy lorries took everything from office records and furniture to the heaviest of workshop equipment the 200 miles to Loughborough. Approximately 60 per cent of the workforce sought a new life in the East Midlands, while the remainder obtained jobs with Westland or elsewhere in the Yeovil area. Despite heavy snow, the massive task was completed by the end of March, having been masterminded by Tommy Keep, director, and Eddie Wrinch, the works manager. Everything from Petters was absorbed into Brush's 35 acre factory, with the West Country labour raising the Loughborough workforce to over 2,500. Petters emerged the same, if different!

Many had previously thought of the East Midlands as an industrial wasteland and were pleasantly surprised to find countryside. The long-established angling club soon found the fast-flowing rivers of Leicestershire provided a different challenge to the placid waters of Somerset. Some still hankered for the sweet smell of the Yeovil countryside, like Bill Webb, a sprightly 70-year-old who regularly cycled back from Loughborough over a weekend to savour his homeland.

The family atmosphere forged in the early days of the company did not fade away; if anything, the departure from Yeovil brought the employees closer together. Obviously, there were problems of integration with the Brush workforce and this was highlighted by Wrinch, the works manager, constantly referring to the Yeovil contingent as 'My boys'. By contrast, Good often referred to the same characters as 'You Petter bastards', when their actions threatened to delay the cohesion of the entire labour force.

Good continued his personal investment expansion by obtaining shares in a diverse range of aircraft, motor and internal combustion engine manufacturers. He soon won the respect of the Petter workforce and while often cursing them as a body, he later praised them publicly and described the Superscavenge engines as 'far ahead of anything on the market'. Further development of the Superscavenge range led to the series V, MkII engines producing 100 hp per cylinder at 600 r/min. Made in two- to six-cylinder form and marketed as the 'Triumph of the Age', they stayed in production until 1951. The Petter engines increased Brush's engine division, whose range now included the Superscavenge, the PU and the recently introduced 'A' series. They also made a Brush diesel known as the Vis-a-vis, a horizontal design that was sold to J. & H. McLaren, in Leeds. Tommy Keep was made managing director of Brush covering all divisions.

Brush had started in business in 1879, when Charles F. Brush, an American manufacturer of arc lamps and dynamos, came to this country to open a London business. That business became Brush Electrical Engineering Co. Ltd with their works in Loughborough. They supplied generators to Petters for their lighting plants and power station projects in the years before the First World War and immediately afterwards. By 1938, Brush were making transformers, switchgear, generating sets, steam turbines, diesel engines and coachwork for railway carriages and passenger road transport.

The hundredth Royal Show took place in July 1939 at Windsor Great Park, and Petters once again showed their products despite the change in ownership and the move. Some Atomic-powered 1 kW and 5.5 kW lighting sets were shown with timely warnings of possible air raids ahead. There was also a 20 hp Atomic and the little A1, billed as the 'Mighty Atom', mounted on a pneumatic-tyred trolley of the type sold to the Air Ministry. Around the show were exhibitors featuring fourteen different applications with Petter engines. Brush were represented on Petters' stand with a homogenizer manufactured by Improved Emulsification Process Co. Ltd, another group company.

Within six months of the move from Yeovil the employees faced another major upheaval – the Second World War. Following Hitler's invasion of Austria in 1938 and Czechoslovakia in the following March, Britain was shocked when

The announcement of the 'Mighty Atom' 'A' type petrol engine of 1.5 to 3 hp, at the Royal Show, Windsor, 1939

Germany invaded Poland on 1 September 1939. An ultimatum calling on Germany's withdrawal from Poland met with no response and therefore, at 11 a.m. on 3 September, Britain, France, Australia and New Zealand declared war on Germany. There had been considerable rumours and scaremongering prior to the outbreak of war. The Emergency Powers Act of August 1939 suspended habeas corpus, the right to free assembly, the right to demonstrate or strike and forebade public dissent. The publication of weather forecasts was discontinued; police in patrol cars were armed with two Lee Enfield rifles and aliens could be detained and sent to internment camps. Initially, provision was made to relocate or mass evacuate some five million people to one of three areas, Evacuation, Neutral or Reception.

Three and a half million people were moved to safer areas by the end of September 1939, but by April 1940, 200,000 of them had moved back because hostilities had not taken place. Britain's Imperial Defence Committee estimated the country would suffer 1.8 million casualties in the first two months of the war, requiring 20 million square feet of timber for coffins. They also forecast 175,000 would die in the first 24 hours. These impossible figures led to ground being earmarked for mass graves and special measures being made for thousands of people deafened for life by the sound of bombing.

A Petter PU8 pumping set made for the army in 1940

A Petter 'A' type air-cooled petrol-engined military air compressor, 1940; similar to the models used for starting aircraft

A Petter 'B' type air-cooled diesel, 1940

In fact, the phoney war lasted from September 1939 to April 1940, when the only hostilities of any significance were in France. Winston Churchill became prime minister on 10 May 1940 and soon factory hours were fixed at 8 a.m. to 7 p.m. and Income Tax was raised from 5s to 7s 6d in the pound.

Britain feared air raids, and it was estimated that for every ton of high explosive dropped there would be fifty casualties. Air raid precaution wardens were created in 1937, with volunteers being paid £3 per week, which was more than the troops received. They were equipped with hooded torches, wooden gas attack rattles and brass handbells, and became adept after the outbreak of war at bellowing, 'Put that light out' whenever the smallest glimmer appeared from a building. The ARP wardens' main task was patrolling during the hours of darkness looking for blackout offences, incendiary bombs or gas attacks. Petters' labour force formed their own ARP group and considerable time was spent in painting white bands around telegraph poles and trees to assist pedestrians and traffic at night in the blackout. Even kerbs, steps, bollards and car running boards received the white outlining. In the cities it was said that some painted the rims of their bowler hats in order to be visible. The countryside was not left out of these precautionary measures, for it was not uncommon to see luminous bows or tail lights attached to cows and other animals being herded along lanes at twilight. Road casualties doubled and there were many accidents with people receiving injury from tripping over kerbs, falling into ditches or into the path of oncoming vehicles. This led to the introduction of Summer Time and later Double Summer Time to lessen the dangers of travelling after dark.

The walls of factory canteens became the ideal place for displaying government posters. The first of these exhorted the workforce to 'Keep Calm and Carry On', 'Defend Freedom with All Your Might' and 'Your Courage, Your Cheerfulness, Will Bring Victory'. Later, similar posters warned 'Careless Talk Costs Lives', or advised 'Dig for Victory'. Many workers were directed to munitions or aircraft factories, while young men of conscription age had the option of becoming 'Bevin Boys' in the coal mines instead of military service.

The Petter horticulturalists became proficient in digging and erecting Anderson air-raid shelters in the gardens of their homes. In addition to the ARP wardens and fire-watchers, many of the workforce became official observers; watching from sandbagged lookouts on factory roof tops, they became efficient in the use of stirrup pumps and putting out incendiary bombs. Other workers joined the Local Defence Volunteers, later to become the Home Guard. In the first 24 hours after the announcement of war, 250,000 men across the nation joined this Dad's Army. Many were armed with privately owned shot-guns, while others had lengths of drainpipe with a 17 in bayonet secured to one end.

As the war progressed, the Brush factory set daily production targets, with the

A 1941 Superscavenge marine diesel
in a Trent Navigation barge

machine shop working double shifts. Civil and export orders for agricultural applications could only be undertaken by special permit from the Ministry of Supply. Eddie Wrinch became works manager and Capt. Dick Petter was placed in charge of engine production, while Tommy Keep was moved to the Ministry of Supply. The Superscavenge engine found a new application in marine form powering minesweepers. The industrial version proved an ideal power unit for portable electrical generating sets used in towns where power stations had been put out of action by bombing.

Petters' machine shop went on to munitions work with the manufacture of sixty-seven Vickers co-axial gun-mountings made from 100 ton bullet-proof steel. The turrets incorporated a two-pounder gun and a Besa machine gun. When the Churchill tank became available, the small gun was replaced with a six-pounder.

As the war continued, and munitions became scarce, army officers were flown from the North African front lines to tour munition factories exhorting workers to produce more. It was not uncommon for welders and machinists to work 72

A Petter 2A wartime gen-set, *c.* 1943

hours with only short meal breaks and brief catnaps beside their machines. Fourteen similar companies worked on the tank-turret project, with production of around two hundred and fifty per week. Petters' were the co-ordinating source responsible for materials and production, with Capt. Dick as chairman of the group. When the American Sherman tank became available to the British troops, the six pounder project was cancelled and so the round-the-clock working ceased.

Eddie Wrinch worked himself to an early death during the massive war effort and died before hostilities were over. Bob Hunter and Bertie Mears, two old Yeovil men, were placed in charge of large and small engine production respectively and continued to operate the works without a replacement works manager. Only two bombs were dropped on Loughborough during the war, probably as a result of German aircraft returning from raids on Rolls-Royce factories at Derby. None of the Loughborough bombs damaged the Brush works.

The Rhine crossing during the Second World War made easier with Petter PU8-powered pontoons, 1944

ABE acquired the share capital of J. & H. McLaren, oil engine manufacturers of Leeds, in 1943 and Mirrlees, Bickerton & Day in 1944. Brush took over the McLaren and Mirrlees operation from ABE in 1949 plus some shares in National Gas & Oil Engine Co., eventually purchasing the remaining shares. Some years later, it was realized that an anomaly existed in that Brush Electrical Engineering Co., Ltd, were operating as manufacturers while acting as a holding company for McLaren, Mirrlees and others. To overcome the anomaly, the name was changed to The Brush Group Ltd, so it became a holding company owning all the shares in Mirrlees, Petters, Brush, etc., while each company continued as manufacturers with their own board of directors. Another new company, with an old name, Brush Electrical Engineering Co. Ltd, was announced to carry on the Loughborough manufacturing as its predecessor had done.

CHAPTER TWELVE

1945–57

A New Era

Throughout the wartime production, A.P. Good, as deputy chairman and managing director of Brush Electrical, lived in a caravan in the factory yard and could be found at almost any time somewhere within the works, a lifestyle that permanently damaged his health.

When peace came in 1945 and the celebrations were over, it was not long before orders for small engines started to pour in, and even the larger Superscavenge engines were oversold. So fast was the recovery that production could not possibly cope with demand. The resources in terms of factories and skilled staff acquired by Good over the years were pressed into operation. McLaren's were given an order for twenty thousand Petter 'A' type petrol engines and commenced making them at their Fazakerley and Poole factories.

A.P. Good created a new marketing organization to sell products from all the engine companies within the Brush Group. This newcomer was Associated British Oil Engines Ltd. ABOE worked as a concessionaire and operated in separate divisions according to engine capacity. The small engine sales division was run by an old Petter employee, John C. Gale, who had been an assistant to Herbert Sammonds in the Yeovil commercial department.

As the world settled down to reconstruction and development once more, an export version of ABOE was formed, known as ABOE (Export) Ltd, with Capt. Dick Petter as its managing director. This new sales company was based at Dukes Court, Dukes Street, St James's, London, later to become part of the administrative buildings of Hawker Siddeley Group Ltd. ABOE (Export) handled the overseas sales of Mirrlees, Petters, McLaren, Petter-Fielding and Meadows engines from $1\frac{1}{2}$ to 2,880 hp, an indication of how successful A.P. Good had been in establishing a near oil engine monopoly. Each company produced a predetermined segment of horsepower within an overall comprehensive range.

The need to know the long-term build requirements of customers, in terms

The original Causeway factory of Lagonda cars at Staines, *c.* 1947

of oil engines, became paramount in Good's mind. He despatched key members of staff to Original Equipment Manufacturers, (OEMs), to discuss their future engine requirements. John Gale was selected to meet UK agricultural and civil engineering OEMs. When these missionaries of commerce returned, their findings were analysed and so emerged a blueprint for the next generation of Petter engines. This was not before time, for Petters were still manufacturing Atomic engines of 5 hp, 10 hp and 20 hp.

Good now reaped the benefit of his activities some twelve years earlier when, at the age of twenty-nine, he had become chairman of Lagonda Cars Ltd, having paid £67,500 plus £4,000 stock to the official receiver in June 1935, the company having failed in the previous April. Bentley Cars had collapsed in 1931 and their famous founder, W.O. Bentley, had been found a position with a five-year contract by Rolls-Royce Cars, which was really to keep him from designing for competitors. Bentley's contract with Rolls was about to expire when Good acquired Lagonda, so he appointed him as chief designer, an act that produced the 3-litre engine and a temporary revival for Lagonda. In March 1947, Good liquidated all his interests in Lagonda to become chairman of Folland Aircraft at Hamble. Lagonda Cars was purchased by David Brown of Aston Martin in September 1947, and the famous Causeway factory closed.

The Causeway factory stood on the site of the home of the American opera

The Lagonda engine shop in the Causeway works showing the low headroom

singer Wilbur Gunn who also had a passion for engineering. In the mid-1800s he built a steam yacht that won a wager for being the fastest boat on the Thames and in 1898 started to build motorcycles in his greenhouse that stood virtually on the corner of Thorpe Road and the Causeway. The motorcycles sold well under the name Lagonda, which arose from Gunn's home in Springfield, Ohio, where it was the Shawnee Indian name for Buck Creek. The motorcycles had success in the Paris–Madrid international cup races and the first Isle of Man Tourist Trophy. Building on these successes, Lagonda turned to three-wheeled vehicles in 1904. Their first four-wheeled car was a 10 hp model followed by a 16 hp developed for racing at Brooklands in 1909. In the following year it won the Moscow to St Petersburg reliability trial.

Good arranged for ABOE to purchase the Causeway factory, although it was a temporary structure built by Lagonda in 1914 with an extremely low headroom of about 3 m. The Ironbarks works opposite was occupied by Bryce Berger, who were already part of the Brush Group. The Brush interest in Bryce related to their expertise in diesel injection equipment and a small vertical oil engine that was absorbed into the group.

Good arranged for his McLaren company in Leeds to take over the Causeway works to manufacture Petter engines under subcontract. Good's international survey of OEMs led to McLaren's being used to develop Petters' new AV engines with the expertise and machine tools left by Lagonda, and in that way the project was completed in less than nine months. Later, the ex-Lagonda workers were integrated with Petter personnel from Loughborough, many of whom moved south when the company relocated.

The AV engines were launched at a massive 'open day' on 14 October 1948. These water-cooled, four-stroke diesels were rated at 3 hp to 10 hp and were the smallest Petter engines since the merger with Brush. The board responsible for the launch was: A.P. Good, chairman of ABE Ltd and ABOE Ltd; Capt. Dick Petter, director; J.A. Evans, commercial director; and John C. Gale, director and sales manager of small engines. The launch included a display of applications made by OEMs who had assisted in the market research. There were twenty-three categories of working exhibits on display at the launch and all were powered by AV engines. Guests were taken on a guided tour of the company's new 6 acre manufacturing facilities flanking the main A30 road.

Roly G.M. Cawson, director and general manager Hamble

The actual transfer of most Petter personnel from Loughborough to Staines was in 1950, and like the move from Yeovil to Loughborough some twelve years earlier, many employees decided to stay in Leicestershire and take employment with other Brush companies or simply retire. Sadly, Robert A. Bruce died on 8 January 1948. He was an old and valued employee who had been of immense help to the company, particularly during the establishment of the Westland aircraft division. The original Petter Yeovil workforce was declining.

There was no massive transfer of plant, machinery and personnel as in 1938, and only a few key personnel moved to Staines. One of the ex-Lagonda men to join Petters was Roly Cawson, a planning engineer, who later became works manager and a director of the company. Later still, he was appointed as general manager of Petters' Hamble, Southampton, factory before returning to Staines once more, where he retired in 1979.

The Fielding horizontal oil engines that Petters had absorbed in Loughborough were redesigned in 1947 and sent to Leeds for production by McLaren's Airedale factory; they consisted of models EH, FH and FH2 of 21 to 80 hp at 400 to 650 r/min, and were marketed as Petter-Fielding.

When the AVA air-cooled version was added to the water-cooled AV in 1950, together with the marine versions of both, they became Petters' best-ever selling engines. Other engines added in 1952 as extensions to the petrol 'A' series included the W1/WP, W1H/W1HP and the PA series in both air- and water-cooled form rated at 13.5 to 19 hp at speeds from 1,400 to 2,000 r/min. Production of Petters' Superscavenge engine continued until 1951, when it was phased out. The engines had been marketed under the Petter name, although they were manufactured by Mirrlees, Bickerton & Day who had taken over the larger engine responsibility for the Brush Group.

The Festival of Britain, 1951, in the Pleasure Gardens of Battersea Park, London, featured a comic animation commissioned by Petters from Roland Emett, the mechanical inventor, in the form of a single machine to do all jobs on a modern farm. The Hogmuddle Rotary Niggler and Fidgeter was 55 ft long, 9 ft wide and stood 22 ft feet high and was a fascinating working exhibit that brought laughter to thousands of visitors throughout the festival.

The same year, 1951, saw the retirement of Herbert Brookes who returned to his native Yeovil. In February 1953, A.P. Good passed away after a long illness, aged 47. He had been the architect of the Brush Group and responsible for the acquisition and merger of some of the best British diesel engine companies. Sir Ernest Petter died in July 1954, followed by Percy fourteen months later; Percy lived to see the culmination of the family firm at Staines with its modern production methods and impressive array of engines. At a special luncheon in his honour, a display of engines caught Percy's eye and after inspecting the

The Petter-commissioned Rowland Emett working animation as shown at the 1951 Festival of Britain, London

products ranging from a Handyman to the latest PAZ1, he said, 'I never thought I should see an engine work on the diesel principle so small as this.'

The historic lunch brought together many of the remaining Petter old employees, including Capt. Dick Petter as managing director, Herbert Brookes, and Bob Norton and Percy Sharp, director and secretary of the Brush Group. Other guests at the luncheon were John Gale, small engine sales manager of ABOE, and John Dacombe, director and general manager of the Brush Service division at Burton-on-the-Wold. The final toast on that occasion was, 'The Founders of Petters'.

Bryce Berger moved to Gloucester in 1954, vacating Ironbarks works at Staines, so allowing Petters to expand production. The expansion included the twin and vee versions of the 'A' type petrol engines and production of the little PAZ1. This 3 hp engine was ideal for cement mixers and the slow-speed maize cutters used in Africa and the Far East. It won a silver medal for the company at the Bath and West Show in 1954, where Petters were also awarded a gold cup for the best trade stand three years in succession. Yet another new range was added in the same year in the form of the 'B' type engines. These had been designed and developed at Loughborough and moved to Staines for production. The 'B' type was produced in one- to four-cylinder specification from 12 hp to 48 hp and was well received by all sections of industry. The marine versions

Capt. Dick Petter, managing
director, receiving the Gold Cup at
the Bath and West Show, 1954

were so good that Petters revived their pre-war floating demonstrations by
having three varying sizes of vessel moored just across the road from the
Causeway and Ironbarks factories on the River Thames.

The Petter Major, Minor and Petterette could be seen anywhere from Staines
to the coastal towns around the Thames estuary demonstrating their 'B' type
engines often under the watchful eye of Jim Layn, who later became sales
manager of Petters' marine division. Jim was known and respected throughout
the marine industry. In 1968 he was elected vice-chairman of the Marine
Engine & Equipment Manufacturers Association, becoming chairman in 1970.

Petters were now becoming very short of production room, so rationalization
of horsepower was applied, resulting in the 'B' types being passed to McLaren at
Leeds in 1955. With the 'B' type went the drawings, tools and a few prototypes
of the PD and PDV range of 16 hp to 108 hp single and vee diesels. These had
been developed at Staines and now were going to Leeds for production. The
absence of these engines allowed major alterations to take place within the
Causeway works, with the roof line being raised from the old Lagonda height of

The Planning Department's model
room showing a section of the
factory in scale model form

c. 3 m to over 9 m. The alterations took two years as the reconstruction
included the removal of many internal walls to obtain large areas of open floor
for the eventual installation of automated machines and production lines. The
upheaval of men and machines was kept to a minimum and did not disrupt
production. This was achieved by planning engineers under the supervision of
Roly Cawson and Bill Stratton and with the aid of a model room where every
detail of the factory and its contents could be seen in miniature. This not only
proved schematic layouts but allowed union leaders and the workforce generally
to see for themselves the impending changes. Percy Petter would have been very
proud.

CHAPTER THIRTEEN

1957–65
Engineers to the World

The early fifties saw great strides in British exports as the factories got into full production. The time had come to seek new markets, consolidate old ones and generally combat overseas competition.

One of the largest postwar markets for Petter diesels was India and through the company's agent, Parry & Co., of Madras, and their nationwide network of subagents and stockists, Petters were able to sell large quantities of AV engines. However, as early as 1947, with the coming of independence, it was realized by the Indian government that although such imports as Petter diesels were important to their infrastructure and economic development, the high cost to foreign exchange could not be sustained.

In 1952 the Indian government levied import duties on small diesels followed by a ban on all imports of engines between 3 hp and 30 hp. ABOE (Export) foresaw the situation and entered into a manufacturing licence with Kirloskar Oil Engines Ltd, of Poona, in 1947. The licence allowed Kirloskar to manufacture Petter AV and B type engines; initially, most of the components were shipped from the UK to be assembled in India. By 1961, when the licence lapsed, the engines were wholly manufactured by Kirloskar who were by that time exporting and therefore in competition with Petters.

There was so much export business to be gained that the Brush Group formed trading companies around the world and had agents in most countries. The strong after-sales service created by Petters was revised to include J. & H. McLaren engines, and a new Service and Spares Centre was opened at Burton-on-the-Wold. Supervised by John Dacombe, the service manager from the Yeovil days, and his assistant, Charlie Munden, the new organization became a valued part of the Brush Group. The centre housed massive stocks of spare parts and could manufacture obsolete components from drawings of engines built in the Vickers-Petter days. John Dacombe retired in 1961 after twenty-four years with Petters and Charlie Munden took charge of the division.

The Petter mobile Service School display van in New York with Jim Branson, left, 1969; a year during which 324 pupils were trained in refrigeration, marine propulsion, air compressor or industrial engine maintenance

A microfilm library housing the details of all components for engines built in the previous forty years was established and a team of forty mobile service engineers was based at Burton. Service schools became a regular feature at Petter agents and stockists with the arrival of a mobile display van and workshop under the control of a service supervisor. These visits were not confined to the UK; many tours were arranged in Europe, the United States and North Africa, mostly with Jim Branson at the wheel of the mobile display van and carrying out the tuition with Roy Leach.

In 1957, Petters experienced another change of ownership when the Brush Group were acquired by Hawker Siddeley Industries Ltd. This conglomerate eventually comprised one hundred and forty-six industrial companies worldwide before they too were acquired. HSI were a wholly owned subsidiary of Hawker Siddeley Group and, as before, Petters and all other Brush companies were allowed to retain their identity. The main products within Hawker Siddeley Group were electrical and diesel, so to promote their strong corporate identity

Petter PC powered concrete saw in use on a military airfield, *c.* 1957

the new sales slogan of 'Engineers to the World' was adopted. This was an accurate claim. HSI had as its chairman Sir Roy Dobson, and Percy Sharp, the ex-Petter and later Brush company secretary, as a director and company secretary.

A.P. Good's idea of segregation of horsepower for the diesel companies within his group was continued by HSI, and in 1958 Petters took back the B and PD series from McLaren, so making their maximum manufactured horsepower 108 hp instead of 20 hp. They also acquired the 13.3 hp to 40 hp Armstrong Siddeley engines, to which were added the PD series and, later, Armstrong badge versions of other Petter engines. Later still, the PJ series became the ASJ and, like other Armstrong engines, were painted light grey instead of the famous mid-Brunswick Green, with the Petter diamond being replaced by a black Sphinx within a diamond shape.

Also in 1958, the Ironbarks factory came into production, adding a further 80,000 sq. ft of space. The new PC series, announced the year before, heralded the era of high-speed, air-cooled engines. These 3,000 r/min, lightweight

The 1957 British Transport Commission 6 ton Scammell tractor with Petter PC4 air-cooled diesel. It was hoped that this urban delivery application would bring orders for 10,000 of the engines and put Petters into the automotive industry

diesels of 5 hp to 20 hp were produced in one- to four-cylinder specification for automotive type applications.

If successful, the engines could have achieved Petters' long-term ambition of becoming a major name within the motor vehicle industry. At one time it was hoped the PC would power London taxis and the new British Transport Commission (now British Rail) three-wheel urban delivery tractors. BTC had ordered some 10,000 of the Scammell tractors and more than 25,000 trailers; together with the taxi application, the combined orders for engines would have been beyond Petters' dreams. However, the PC and the PCM marine version proved unreliable due to injector and cooling problems and were soon phased out.

Considerable extension and improvement was made to the Causeway, Ironbarks and Bridge works during the late fifties under Ken Fraser, the new managing director, aided by the resources of HSG. Causeway's production area was expanded to 342,000 sq. ft. In 1958, *The Engineer* magazine reviewed the company's manufacturing facilities as they had periodically done throughout Petters' long history. They reported that the company were part way through a five-year rebuilding programme designed to accommodate an increased range of products with better natural lighting and improved floor loading, while easing access within the Causeway factory. The magazine highlighted the installation of the 'Wheelabrator' shot-blasting of castings and the 'Planetomat' machining system for producing finished overhead valve rocker arms from forged steel components.

Petters signed an agreement in 1958 with Thermo King Corporation of Wisconsin, USA, to manufacture transport refrigeration units under licence; the units were designed for road-, rail- and sea-going insulated containers and marketed as Petter Transport Refrigeration Units. The units were manufactured at the old Avro Hamble factory that had been acquired by HSI, later to be integrated with Petters, and were powered by internal combustion engines, hydraulic motors or electrical supply to provide automatic heating or cooling for perishable cargoes. They could safeguard the cargo regardless of outside ambient temperatures changing from tropical heat to Arctic cold. In later years, the Petter AA1, the first of the aluminium diesels, and its following derivatives were used to power some of the company's transport refrigeration units.

The Service, Spares and Service School moved from Burton to join Petters Transport Refrigeration Units and other products in 1961. The move took six months to complete and Roly Cawson moved from Staines to Hamble to become director and general manager. The Burton works became part of Petters' network of service depots under the managership of John McLean, Staines; Norman Grimes, Hamble; Jack Fawcett, Burton; Arthur Barradell, Leeds; Jack Kirkwood, Glasgow; and Roy Skinner, Aberdeen.

The additional nine-hundred Hamble employees were a useful if difficult acquisition for Petters. Useful, for the added production and storage areas were readily available, but difficult, because of the 64 miles separating them from Staines. There was also a problem of compatibility. Whereas the previous mergers with Brush, Lagonda and Bryce Berger had been a natural integration there were now difficulties. The Hamble factory marinized the company's industrial engines, produced the transport refrigeration units, Petter air compressors, and custom-made generating sets up to 1,000 kVA. A massive spares facility for obsolete engines was also located there, with parts being available for Petter-Fielding horizontal oil engines, Atlantic, Fowler, Coventry Cub, Brush, McLaren and even the old Coborn petrol engines.

The old Avro aircraft works built in 1916 with slip access to Southampton Water was once the centre of several long-distance aviation record attempts carried out by Burt Hinkler, Avro's chief test pilot until 1928. The original

A Petter AVA2 powered sawbench on a forestry estate, *c.* 1960

A typical B1 powered conveyor, *c.* 1960

airfield had long since been developed as a giant oil storage tank farm by Shell while the additional 100 acres on the other side of Hamble Lane was a flying training school operated by Air Service Training Ltd. AST moved there in 1931 shortly before Avro vacated the factory and were responsible for training many Battle of Britain pilots and, later, thousands of civil airline pilots before moving from the site in 1960.

Hawker Siddeley Aviation (ex-HS Aircraft, 1935) comprised A.V. Roe, Sir W.G. Armstrong Whitworth, Armstrong Siddeley Motors, Gloster Aircraft, Hawker Aircraft and Air Service Training, a position that had enabled them to supply 30 per cent of the RAF's wartime engine and aircraft requirement. In 1963, they acquired Folland Aircraft Ltd at Hamble, an acquisition that had a dramatic effect on the last of the Petter inventors. W.E.W. (Teddy) Petter, then aged 52, gave up his position as managing director and chief executive of Folland to seek a contemplative life searching for fundamental truth.

W.E.W. Petter had left his family's firm of Westland late in 1944, after disagreement over his constant interference with production which was something the new owners, John Brown, could not tolerate, as he was a designer. He was given the choice of two designs he was working on to take to English Electric in Lancashire, where he was to be chief engineer. Teddy selected the bomber design which became the Canberra, probably Britain's first pure jet bomber, of which 1,100 were made. He stayed at English Electric until the late fifties, when he resigned over a disagreement concerning experimental facilities. From there he moved to Folland, where he invested his money and became their managing director.

At Folland, Teddy Petter created the Gnat jet fighter-trainer in 1965, an aircraft used for fifteen years by the RAF's Red Arrow display team until 1980. When he left the industry he wrote to his lifelong friend and flying instructor, Harald Penrose, saying, 'Science has been desecrated to become the tool of financial manipulators. They worship nothing but power and money, so Claude [his Franco-Swiss wife] and I are going to live a simple life of prayer and meditation.'

They moved to a small hotel near Lausanne where, clad in monk-like habits, they lived just such a life. Later, Teddy and Claude moved to France, where he died in 1968, a tragic loss to aviation and the end of a family of great inventors. Teddy Petter's father, Sir Ernest, had once remarked to Penrose on the occasion of Teddy learning to fly, 'I wish you'd teach him to sow a few wild oats instead.' One cannot help thinking that if such had been the case, how much our history might have altered.

The early sixties was an unproductive era for the Hamble factory, for Hawker Siddeley had no real product to build there. An experimental racing catamaran

Rotary machining of Petter 'A' series aluminium cylinder heads

Multiple drilling of a PH1 crankcase

A typical PH1 powered dumper. This engine and its larger twin version became almost standard equipment in this type of application during the sixties

in glass-fibre was produced and a number of pre-fabricated bus shelters assembled. However, the slipway at Avro's old factory was put to good use by the employees' sailing club and their Sports & Social Clubhouse was the envy of Staines for many years before similar facilities were built next to the Ironbarks canteen. There were many attempts to integrate the two workforces with the exchange of personnel and inter-factory social activities. These did little to overcome the prejudice that existed between the two workforces.

In the sixties, Petters' Staines factories suffered from overcrowding and a general lack of production space. Many planning applications were made to the local authority for expansion but most of these were rejected for the site bordered the A30 with its annual holiday traffic to the West and periodic race meetings at Ascot, so there were many restrictions. To create publicity and promote local awareness, the company tried to acquire sponsorship of the roundabout in front of the main office block facing Staines Bridge over the Thames. The suggestion was to landscape and florally maintain the roundabout but this generous offer also met with no success. However, they did gain permission to build on the triangle of land to the side of Ironbarks factory sandwiched between the railway line and the Chertsey Road. On that triangle

A GRP racing catamaran made at Petters' Hamble factory, *c.* 1960

Portable bus shelters made at Petters' Hamble factory, *c.* 1960

they built the R&D Centre, probably the first specifically designed for research into air-cooled, high-speed diesels. The R&D site also contained the employees' car and cycle park; this was a problem if one worked at the far end of the Causeway factory, for it was half a mile away!

The centre opened in 1962, having been designed by John Smith, Petters' technical director, and managed by Joe Joseph, an ex-apprentice. It measured 129 m (207 ft) long and 72.5 m (116 ft) wide and housed the design, development and administrative offices on the first floor, and workshops and testing facilities on the ground floor. There were six test cells with two sprung-mounted testbeds for engines up to 50 hp and two cells for engines of up to 300 hp. Each cell received three different supplies of fuel and two of lubricating oil. Complete research programmes could be carried out from the remote-control monitoring panels. Two further test cells provided simulation of tropical heat complete with dust storms and Arctic cold with temperatures down to −40° C.

A PJ4 air-cooled diesel undergoing trials in an R&D test chamber

The test-cell monitoring booths in Petters' R&D Centre, *c.* 1966

The centre started on the design of the next generation of Petters' diesels to meet the constant demand for engines with more power and less weight. This led to the PJ range with its performance of 11.25 hp per cylinder as opposed to the AV/AVA of 6 hp per cylinder produced fifteen years previously. The PJs were a natural progression from the AV/AVA engines first produced in 1946 and the PH/PHW engines that followed. The PJ were cast-iron, air- and water-cooled engines made in one- to four-cylinder specification and producing up to 45 hp at 2,000 r/min.

Extensive research work into ways of raising combustion efficiency without affecting the temperature of the injectors was carried out and there evolved an entirely new concept of engines manufactured largely from aluminium. Using the unique Lanova air/fuel cell combustion system, this new breed of engines first appeared as the AA1 in 1964 and for many years was the smallest and lightest diesel in the world. These lightweight, high-speed, air-cooled engines featured bellhousings over their flywheels, so making close-coupling to generators, welding sets and gearboxes easier. In 1966, the company received the

Petter AA1 gen-set in use with the Australian National Antarctic Research Expedition, 1970

The new Petter AA1 single cylinder air cooled diesel of 1.5 to 3.5 bhp at 1,900 to 3,600 rev/min, undergoing cold starting tests in the research centre at Staines. This engine represents a major advance in design to reduce size and weight, extensive use being made of light alloys. It is the smallest diesel in the world with a continuous output of 3.5 bhp.

Artificial cold weather trials for an engine in Petters' arctic test chamber, 1964

Queen's Award to Industry for the AA1 and the company's 'technological innovation in diesel engine design'.

In the overseas market, Hawker Siddeley International were concerned at the impending cessation of the manufacturing licence with Kirloska in 1961. Some years before the acquisition of Brush by HSI, the National Gas & Oil Engine Co., part of the Brush Group, had made an agreement with Mahindra & Mahindra Ltd, of Calcutta, to form the Indian National Diesel Engine Co. Ltd. The purpose was to locally produce some of National's range. Subsequently, it was possible for HSI, with the co-operation of the Indian government, to create the Indian National Diesel Engine Co. Ltd from the Mahindra & Mahindra operation. In addition to manufacturing National engines, it was agreed the new company should also make selected air-cooled models.

For a year, many Petter planning engineers found themselves in the heat of Calcutta developing jigs and tools to suit local climatic conditions and training local labour. Eventually, the production of PH single- and twin-cylinder

The Queen's Award to Industry
presented to Petters Ltd in 1966
for 'technological innovation in
diesel engine design'

ELIZABETH THE SECOND,

by the Grace of God of the United Kingdom of Great Britain and Northern Ireland and of Our other

Realms and Territories Queen Defender of the Faith, to

PETTERS LTD.

Greeting!

We being cognisant of the industrial efficiency of the said body as manifested in Technological

Innovation and being desirous of showing Our Royal Favour do hereby confer upon it

THE QUEEN'S AWARD TO INDUSTRY

for a period of five years from the 21st day of April 1966 until the 20th day of April 1971 and

do hereby give permission for the authorised flag of the said Award to be flown during that time

by the said body and for the device thereof to be displayed upon letters and communications

of the said body and upon its packages and goods in the manner authorised by Our Warrant

of the 30th day of November 1965.

And We do further hereby authorise the said body during the five years of the currency of this

Our Award further to use and display in like manner the flags and devices of any former such

Awards by it received.

Given at Our Court at St. James's under Our Royal Sign Manual this 21st day of April in the

year of Our Lord 1966 in the Fifteenth year of Our Reign.

By the Sovereign's Command

Harold Wilson.

The Queen's Award to Industry citation

Petter PH series cylinder barrels
being matched to pistons

engines, with 50 per cent local component manufacture, was achieved in early
1962.

Back at home, an application for office development received approval. The
company had wanted to build an administration block on the site of Bridge
works, but when this was rejected they submitted plans for a third-floor
extension to Ironbarks works over the existing office area above the main
entrance. This required a lift to be installed for A.E. Masters, the managing
director, who was in poor health and needed assistance to reach the boardroom.
The winding gear room extended above the agreed skyline so revised planning
permission had to be sort. When the alterations to the building were complete,
a neon Petter Diamond was added to one side of the facia, while on the other
was a similar electric sign bearing the words, 'Hawker Siddeley Diesels'.

In addition to the AV/AVA, PH/PHW, PJ/PJW and PAZ1 engines being
built at this time, Petters made the W1 laboratory test engine that was supplied
as standard equipment to all oil and research companies. The engines were used

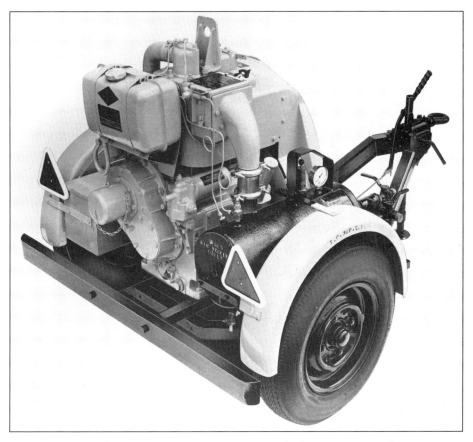

A Petter PJ50 portable air compressor using a PJ2 engine as both power source and compressor

by the leading oil research companies for testing their products to Ministry of Supply specification DEF 2101B relating to oils for British Services, the US military specification MIL-L-2104A and British Standards specification BS1905:1952 for engine lubrication oil (HD) type.

Petter Compressors were developed from the products of Air Pumps Ltd of Raynes Park, a company acquired by Petters in 1963. They were portable and stationary air compressors ranging from 75 cfm to 600 cfm.; the PJ50/PJ75 used adapted PJ2/PJ4 engines to produce compressed air from one or two cylinders while the others provided the power, an idea first used by Petters at the turn of the century. Petters' marine division specialized in air-cooled diesels for ships' lifeboats and workboats, while the larger PJ water-cooled units found satisfied users in Trinity House for their supply-ship launches. The Petter generating-set

Inspection of Petter PH crankshafts

The pre-delivery check of the 'A' series, PH and BA series engines in the Causeway factory, 1972

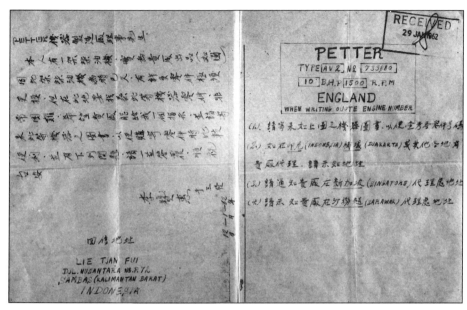

A series of strangely addressed airmail letters received by Petters at Staines, proving the company was well known to the postal authorities

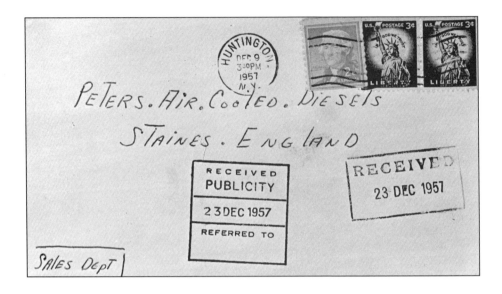

division, also located at Hamble, came into its own in 1971 under the new managership of Alister Monkhouse. Alister had been with the company for twenty years and enjoyed excellent contracts administration experience and now headed the division making portable and stationary generating sets up to 1,000 kVA using Petter, Rolls-Royce, Dorman and Cummins engines.

The Causeway works at Staines were always an arresting sight, with their seemingly endless conveyor lines of engines in varying stages of assembly flanked by sub-assembly bays and what seemed like acres of component machining. Visitors were always impressed by the seemingly countless racks of crankshafts and the spectacular heat treatment by induction hardening of those components. Another impressive and interesting sight was at the far end of the works, for everything progressed in that direction, where mountains of engines were housed in the automatic Triax storage system. Next to that system was the despatch bay where stacks of export cases with stencilled destinations read like a world atlas. Every day, a fleet of Petter lorries and trailers rolled out of the Causeway factory delivering pallets of engines to UK OEMs or cased engines for export. Sometimes the exports went by lorry to the British Waterways docks at Brentford where they were offloaded on to barges for the journey down the Thames to ships loading in one of London's docks. Some 50 per cent of Petters' production was direct exports, with a further 25 per cent finding its way abroad as part of OEM exports. The man co-ordinating the paperwork was Nick Hollick, Petters' shipping manager, who also acted as the company's translator and interpreter. Nick also carried out the vital business of masterminding air flight itineraries for the directors and senior executives around the world.

The worldwide use of Petter engines led to some unusually addressed letters from overseas customers being received. Three examples sent between 1957 and 1962 were addressed using just a copy of an engine plate; Peter Air Cooled Diesels; and 'Petter when writing quote engine number'; all arrived safely!

The Staines workforce was an amalgam of employees from previous company locations. A few came from Yeovil, others had transferred from sister Brush companies, while the remainder were local Staines people who had worked with Lagonda or Bryce Berger. The few remaining Yeovil employees included John C. Gale, A.D. (Peter) Kent, Ken White, Norman Grimes, Percy Swetman, Cyril Hawker, Sid Meech, Reggie Lang and, of course, Percy Sharp at HSI headquarters.

CHAPTER FOURTEEN

1965–79

Together Again

Hawker Siddeley announced the acquisition of R.A. Lister & Co. Ltd, of Dursley, in 1965. Listers had been one of Petters' largest competitors in the UK and now both companies were part of Hawker Siddeley Diesels. This division comprised Petters, Listers, Mirrlees National, Lister Blackstone and Gardners, representing a massive production of diesel power from $1\frac{1}{2}$ hp to 8,500 hp, much of it allied to power generation.

The prospect of Hawker Siddeley Diesels becoming a reality in terms of marketing was not welcomed by British OEMs because they saw a possibility of a cartel. In 1966, the OEM trade association indicated their members' fears to HSG with the statement that they would buy engines from Europe or the Far East if HSG merged Lister and Petters. The timing of this coincided with the opening of the Construction Equipment Exhibition at Crystal Palace, where Petters and the majority of OEMs were exhibiting. Hawkers quickly confirmed that no rationalization would take place within twenty years and both companies would continue to sell in competition with one another.

After a long illness and increasing periods of almost total inability to work, A.E. Masters, CB, CBE, MIMechE, retired as Petters' managing director in 1966. He had come to Petters from the Ministry of Defence, Fighting Vehicle Research and Development Establishment at Chobham, where he had been director. Eddie Masters died on 7 June 1968, aged sixty-five. The company held a memorial service for him at St Paul's parish church, Egham, where a large representation from the armed forces, Ministry of Defence and the company attended.

In a foreword to a short history document produced by the author in 1965 for *Hawker Siddeley News*, Eddie Masters had praised the workforce with the following message:

Three Score Years and Ten has often been quoted as man's expected life span. The '70 Years of Progress' experienced by Petters Ltd has shown many simi-

A.E. Masters, managing director
1960–67

larities to human life and so it should, for thousands of lives have created this company of ours. The beginning, centred around Petters' family, gave a closely knit union so vital in the early days of any company. Over the years this feeling of unison and common purpose has been strengthened by the years of service devoted to the company by employees' families.

Now nearing the completion of our 70th year we are far from reaching the end of an era, for the introduction of new products, Air Pumps compressors, Thermo King transport refrigeration units, etc., has spread the business potential to many fields. Backed by the strength of HSG and the added interest in diesel power provided by Mirrlees National and R.A. Lister, we can look forward with a forceful and mature outlook. The introduction of our latest range of aluminium constructed diesels, from one of the finest Research Centres in Europe, demonstrates that we are a forward thinking company, capable of pioneering new methods of operation and construction. We look forward to consolidating our lead in this field with the extension of this range. I would like to thank all employees and in particular those remaining from the 'Yeovil Days' for their service over these eventful years.

The Petter board of directors and senior executives, 1965: left to right, Bill Stratton, director and works manager; Jack Waterman, chief inspector; W.H. Rees, deputy MD; George Owen, financial director and company secretary; A.E. Masters, managing director; John Smith, technical director; Roly G.M. Cawson, director; John C. Gale, director and home sales manager; Hugh Marsden, personnel manager; Ron H. Kennedy, purchasing manager

An aerial view of Petters' Hamble factory, *c.* 1969

W.H. Rees, deputy chairman and
managing director 1967–74

When W.H. Rees strode through the entrance to Petters in 1967 as newly appointed managing director, everyone took a deep breath for the energy and dynamic sense of purpose could be sensed even from the distance of the directors' car park. Bill Rees came to Petters at a time of high industrial unrest, not only at the company's Staines and Hamble factories but throughout Britain.

Born in South Africa in 1920, Bill Rees had joined the company in 1966 as deputy managing director waiting for Eddie Masters to retire. He came to Petters from HS International where he had been on the board of Industrial Power, and was vice-chairman of the British Combustion Engines Manufacturers Association. He had a great interest in trade associations. The unions within Petters quickly realized that he could be trusted and was fair in all his dealings. Despite an intense workload, he found time to walk at least once a week through the works and offices, pausing here and there to discuss matters with shop stewards or merely to enquire about a worker's family or share a recent social occasion; this attribute more than anything else endeared him to many. He possessed a phenomenal memory for faces, names and personal detail,

Hydraulically operated automatic brick unloading powered by a Petter AA1, *c.* 1965

The Despatch and Shipping Department of Petters' Causeway factory, 1971

Automatic grinding of AA1 crankshafts, *c.* 1970

all of which led to extremely good labour relations. His interest in the social activities of the Staines and Hamble workforce brought him closer to the people than any other director since the retirement of the Petter twins. As deputy chairman and managing director of Petters in 1970, he put up 'The Chairman's Putter', the prize for the annual golf tournament between the Staines and Hamble factories, and cups for the best apprentice at both factories. He also exercised his communication skills with overseas agents and travelled widely to meet them and their families. Often these meetings were combined with a game of golf, at which he and the export sales manager, Jack Regis, who often accompanied him, were no mean players.

The mid-sixties were boom years for the construction industry at home and overseas. Petters took part in international trade fairs around the world, sometimes as an individual company and at others in conjunction with agents or as part of a Department of Trade & Industry joint venture within a British

A series engines being assembled and tested in the Causeway factory, 1972

Pavilion. They also opened a sales office in Lake Success, Long Island, New York, managed by Paul D. Pritchard and staffed by Sid Bishop, Paul Starr and Dick Baker. In 1976, Onan, an American manufacturer of engines and generating sets, and a member of Hawker Siddeley Group, took over the sales of Petter in the USA. In 1984, Petter Diesel Inc. opened an office in Tucker, Georgia, and a joint manufacturing exercise commenced in South Africa with Petter Diesel (Proprietary) SA. The sales of Lister-Petter Ltd in the USA are now conducted by Lister-Petter Inc., Kansas.

Production difficulties in the late sixties led to extended deliveries, until customers were being offered forty-eight months lead time. All advertising was cancelled, with Petters disappearing from trade journals for eight years. As the sixties drew to a close there was an obvious change taking place in traditional markets. A wealth of small diesel engines from French, German, Italian and Japanese manufacturers made sales to OEMs more difficult. Petters were facing their traditional problem of stocking large numbers of variants for customers'

Portable lighting tower, *c.* 1985

A gen-set application in the Caribbean

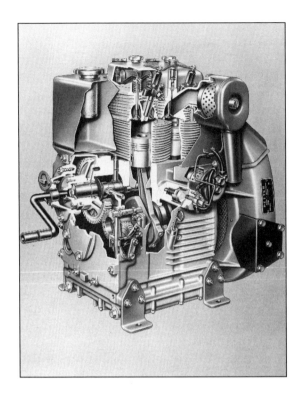

Cutaway view of a Petter BA2 air-
cooled diesel

individual specifications, leading to disruption of production line continuity and
heavy financial investment. For the third time in their history they restricted
build specifications to basic models, with a selection of 'model-build kits'
available for customers to produce their required form of drive. In reality, this
usually meant the company carrying out the work, in effect reworking the
stock-built engines.

The sales of petrol engines for horticultural applications were on the increase, so
to tap into this market, Petters acquired the business of MAG engines, a small
Swiss-made range of petrol, four-stroke motors of 4 to 17 hp in single- and twin-
cylinder form. The Petter-MAG engines were ideal for most municipal equipment.

The company won first prize for the best stand at the Institute of
Groundsmanship Exhibition, Motspur Park, where they showed the Petter-
MAG engines for the first time. However, the engines were difficult to sell in
this specialized market dominated by the more popular American and Japanese
makes, and within a few years the company ceased the marketing arrangement.

In 1967 J.W. Stagg, founder and manager of Petters transport refrigeration
division, retired, so bringing to an end a relationship between the company and

GIFT OF PETTERS' MODEL ENGINE

The author presenting a scale model Petter oil engine on behalf of J.C. Gale to the Curator of the Yeovil Museum, 1968

A detailed scale model of the last engine to be built by Petters Ltd. when the firm was in business in Yeovil was handed over to the Curator of Yeovil Museum, Mr. E. A. Batty (right), on Tuesday, by Mr. K. I. Gibbons, public relations officer, on behalf of Mr. J. C. Gale, director and home sales manager of Petters Ltd., which now operates from Staines, in Middlesex.

his family that dated back to before 1895, when their first engine was used to power a horseless carriage. Bill Stagg's father had been an apprentice with Petters at that time and was required to carry a red flag and walk in front of the vehicle as demanded by the Locomotive Act. George Hancock succeeded him as refrigeration manager, having been with the company's contracts department for some years.

The rising cost of petrol was beginning to cause the public to look at diesel power for private cars and boats, and Volkswagen were one of the first to produce a small diesel engine for their Golf car. Petters examined the VW engine and decided it was ideal for their marine market and so gained Volkswagen's approval to marinize the unit.

Petters decided to extended their range of aluminium, high-speed, air-cooled diesels, initiated by the AA1 in 1964. The new engines were a result of considerable work by Ted Burroughs, chief designer, Ted Coplin, chief engineer, and John Purcell, design engineer, and comprised the AB1, the AC1 and AC2 of 5 hp, 7 hp and 14 hp respectively; water-cooled marine versions of

Petter AB1 powered high-pressure pump
applying insecticides in the Tropical
House at Kew Gardens, 1969

A Petter AB1 air-cooled diesel
showing the Queen's Award to
Industry emblem, 1966

A Petter BA1 shrouded in lead
undergoing noise evaluation tests in
the R&D anechoic test chamber

all of them were added at a later date. Alongside the 'A' series development were
the aluminium DA1, BA1 and BA2 engines, though the DA1 was dropped after
a short period as its performance was closely matched by the smaller and more
powerful AC1.

The AA1 had a difficult early life due to non-acceptance by the building trade
who used notoriously traditional site labourers to start and maintain engines on
hired plant. Unfortunately, the AA1 was not traditional as it required manual
priming in cold weather carried out by an inconspicuous device. Failure to use this
method caused great difficulty in starting. The difficulties in starting the engine in
cold weather resulted in the OEM trade association sending a letter of complaint to
the company. The letter condemned the AA1 and confirmed their members'
concern over the engine's design. There followed a concentrated educational
programme by Petters to instruct the trade in the correct method of starting. This
overcame the problem and the A series went on to become the workhorse of the
building trade with most small site equipment being developed around the engines
by OEMs to provide horsepower for jobs previously carried out by muscle-power.

A PJ4 standby gen-set in a Post Office Telecommunications sub-station, *c.* 1973

All Petters' aluminium engines, except the BA, were designed for continuous operation at 3,000–3,600 r/min, making them ideal for 50 or 60 cycle electrical generation; the BA was restricted to 3,000 r/min. The priming/starting problem experienced with the A series was overcome on the BA series by an automatic decompressor with manual primer. Work on a further series, the CA type, progressed in the R&D Centre, with multi-cylinder versions being produced for testing and evaluation, but did not go into production.

In 1969, Sir Arnold Hall became Petters' chairman, with Bill Rees as deputy chairman and managing director; J.D. (Jack) Regis joined the board as director and overseas sales manager. In the early seventies staff at Staines were shocked to see Bill Rees looking very ill on his return after a Far East sales tour. His normal dynamic appearance and energy had gone and he appeared to have aged considerably. There followed an extended period of absence from the office while he recovered from a supposed stomach bug. Eventually, he returned to his duties but was a changed man and obviously still very ill. Bill Rees died of cancer in 1974, aged fifty-four, a cruel blow that robbed his family and the company of an extremely talented and good man. One of his last major export drives came in 1972, when he concluded a deal with Frans van Bodegraven of

George Owen, director and company secretary (right), and the author, receive the *Financial Times* photography Export Award, 1971

The author welcomes HRH the Princess Margaret to the Hawker Siddeley Group stand, International Trade Fair, Teheran, 1969

A typical temperature-controlled articulated road trailer with Petter PDL50 transport refrigeration unit, *c.* 1972

A selection of Petter portable
air compressors, *c.* 1973

Jack D. Regis, director and export
sales manager, 1969–86

Rotterdam. They had long been established as a Dutch agent for Petters and
now became Petter Continental BV, with a modern works alongside Rotterdam
harbour.

A few years later, Jack Regis, always the keen sportsman and liked by
customers and workforce alike, developed cancer of the throat and, despite
extensive treatment with the latest medical advances, died in 1989. Jack joined
the Brush Group in 1949 and became personal assistant to Petters' managing
director in 1956. Three years later, he was posted to Mexico as vice-president of
Petter-Armstrong Co., returning to England in 1962 to become assistant sales
manager. He was appointed export sales manager in 1966 and boosted the
company's exports during the late sixties, leading to his joining the board as a
director. His keen interest in Petters' social activities often made him the
company's representative at all types of interdepartmental events and
competitions.

E.D. (Dougie) Dettmer, DFC, was appointed managing director of Petters on
1 April 1974, having been with Hawker Siddeley Dynamics Engineering Ltd;

The Petter Continental BV works in Rotterdam, 1973

Petter PH1W marine engines in wooden canoes on Lake Malawi, *c.* 1973

The 1904 Handyman in the
entrance hall of Petters'
R&D Centre, *c.* 1975

he was later transferred to a Far East appointment within the HS Group. A major reorganization of management followed, with the appointment of several young managers from outside the engine trade. Petters continued without an MD until 1979, when Barrie Harper, ex-HSI Brussels, was appointed as sales director for engines, later assuming many of the MD's duties.

By 1979, the company and the order intake situation had changed, and gone were the waiting lists of customers for engines. Petters continued to push model-build specifications, leading to the need for more storage space for stock engines. No. 4 factory was leased at the far end of The Causeway, close to the newly constructed M3 motorway and situated on what had been part of Petters' sports ground. Over four thousand engines were stored in this and other buildings around Staines, many requiring later reworking to suit eventual orders.

Departmental managers changed rapidly as new appointments were made. David Teague came from outside the industry to be appointed sales manager – export. John Smith, Petters' director of engineering, retired after a brilliant career, during which he was responsible for the design of the company's R&D Centre and the introduction of aluminium engines.

John Smith, director of engineering,
1960–79

The Petter PJ4WRMR marine propulsion unit as used by Trinity House for their lighthouse
supply vessel launches, c. 1972

An aerial view of Petters' Staines factory complex, *c.* 1978, showing the R&D Centre, Ironbarks, Causeway and Bridge works

John Stevens, who joined the company in 1966 as a development engineeer and later became research manager, was appointed technical director in July 1979. This could be considered the first stage of merger between Petters and Lister for he was later also appointed as their technical director and is now in the same post at Lister-Petter Ltd.

Feelings of instability persisted at the Hamble and Staines factories as redundancies reduced the combined workforce of two thousand to below nine hundred. The situation was symptomatic of most engine manufacturers in Britain, reflecting the worldwide decline in small engine requirements with an over-capacity for manufacture. Hawker Siddeley Group realized the changing markets and their excessive capacity of diesel power, and increasingly turned their attentions to other spheres of engineering.

Petters stepped back in time in 1979 when they took an active part in what was probably the first one thousand stationary engine rally, held on 16–17 June at Longleat. Organized by *The Stationary Engine* magazine and its editor, David

J.C. Gale, director and home sales
manager, Petters' longest-serving
director

Edgington, enthusiasts and collectors brought their prized and restored exhibits
from all parts of the country. The author attended this historic occasion to
present special T-shirts and hats to exhibitors of early Petter engines. It was the
last time he was to meet John Gale who had come out of retirement to savour
the event.

John C. Gale had given a lifetime of service to Petters. Born *c.* 1900, he had
experienced all the changes, the moves and diversities of product. He started
with the company in its Yeovil days as personal assistant to Herbert Sammonds.
When Sammonds left to join Armstrong Whitworth, John remained in Petters'
commercial department. He moved with the company to Loughborough and
later became a principal part of A.P. Good's survey of OEMs leading to the
design of the AV/PH engines. On moving with the company to Staines, he
became sales manager for small engines and later joined the board as director
and home sales manager. John imparted a presence and bearing wherever and
whenever he represented Petters throughout his long career. He was respected
by his staff, his fellow directors and customers throughout the agricultural

The AC1Z compact of 6 bhp at 3,000 r/min, that replaced the cast-iron PAZ1

A Petter PH2 air-cooled diesel of 19.8 bhp at 2300 r/min

machinery and construction industries. He left the company in the mid-seventies, to enjoy a long retirement in Hazelbury Plucknett before his death in December 1993.

Another man remembered for his contributions to the company who was also present at that historic rally was Norman Grimes. A renowned collector and restorer of vintage motorcycles, he was for many years Petters' service depot manager at Staines before taking over the Spares & Service division at Hamble. When Norman retired the division moved to Staines, where it was accommodated in Causeway and Bridge works. Petters opened a transport refrigeration service depot at Houghton Regis in 1979.

CHAPTER FIFTEEN

1979–95
The Way Ahead

T.D. (Trevor) Davies was appointed managing director in 1979 and served with the company until 1985, handing over the responsibility for the merger with Listers to Stan Keyworth, ex-managing director of Dorman Diesels.

The late seventies saw the rise of Paul Starr to sales manager status. Paul had joined the company as a craft-apprentice in 1964 and on completion of his training moved to Petters' USA sales team in Lake Success, New York, where he carried out technical liaison before becoming responsible for area sales in Houston. Paul returned to the UK in 1976 as sales manager for the south of England. By 1979, he had progressed to sales administration manager for Europe, followed by worldwide responsibility in 1980, becoming general sales manager in March 1985. He is now sales and marketing manager for Lister-Petter Ltd.

Petters received a Council of Industrial Design Award in 1979. The award was 'for significant advancement in small diesel engine design', and related to the AC2 air-cooled diesel developed from the original award-winning single-cylinder AA1 in 1964.

In the following year, 1980, Listers' and Petters' generating set divisions were merged to become Hawker Siddeley Power Plant, located at Lister's Thrupp factory near Stroud; the site now occupied by Alan Sutton Publishing, publishers of this book. A similar exercise was carried out with the marine business of both companies, resulting in Hawker Siddeley Marine. Slowly, the two firms were coming together.

Times were changing, and the shrinking world market for diesel engines in the late seventies and early eighties was exacerbated by the increasing use of hydraulic drive power-take-offs. Some construction site equipment had hydraulic pto to drive additional machines that would otherwise have had their own engines. There was little chance of diesel sales emulating the prosperous period of the fifties and sixties. More and more foreign manufacturers seemed to be competing for a declining market. Lister and Petter both required funding

A Petter AC2 air-cooled diesel of 13.2 bhp at 3600 r/min and winner of a COID award

from Hawker Siddeley to design, develop and introduce new engines, but the group felt that was unwise. Expenditure of the size required to design and launch two new engines in the light of restricted markets was out of the question. However, Hawker Siddeley did provide sufficient funds for the two companies to produce a single design with individual features to be marketed under their respective names. There followed a coming together of the two company's technical staff to establish the design of this hybrid engine and regular meetings took place from 1980. Design and development work continued apace throughout the next eighteen months, resulting in the Petter P600 running for the first time in March 1982. On 1 October of the following year, John Stevens became technical director of Lister and Petter, to combine the expertise and development skills of both companies. Hawker Siddeley directed that the successful Petter AA1 aluminium engine should also be marketed by R.A. Lister & Co., and so the LP1 was announced in 1983.

Assembly of Petter AC2 air-cooled diesels, 1976

Engineers from Staines started to spend more time at Dursley working with their Lister counterparts on the P600 and the Lister version designated the TL. On 2 April 1984, Ted Burroughs, chief engineer, and John Purcell, design engineer, moved to Dursley permanently. Others followed during the year, with the move being complete by 1985.

The Lister TL was announced first, followed by the Petter P600 in 1984. The P600 was an air-cooled design of two- and three-cylinder configuration operating at 3,000 r/min, and produced 10.4 kW to 28 kW of power; all engine rating by this time was stated in kW. The engine owed its development to the experience gained with the PK3 derivative of the PJ range and in particular the cross-flow cylinder head of the BA engine. The engine shared a common crankcase and crankshaft with the Lister TL but differed in several ways, the most significant being the use of a gear lubricating oil pump where the TL relied on a plunger pump. There were also bellhousing adaptations for direct SAE coupling, making the P600 ideal for alternator, water-pump and the 3 ton dumper markets. The P600 offered three mounting positions for hydraulic

A Simplite Spate high-pressure water pump of the type used aboard Royal Navy ships as a portable fire-fighting appliance during the Falkland War

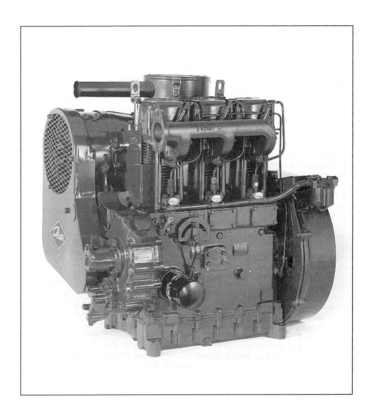

The Petter P600/3
air-cooled diesel
engine

pump drive to cater for the dumper application and featured a belt-driven axial cooling fan rather than integral flywheel blades. The typical diesel knock at low speed was greatly reduced by the use of controlled expansion pistons and the engine had excellent low fuel consumption, with no problems of starting at low temperature. Even the P600/3 could be hand-cranked at temperatures down to −5°C. The engine was intended to complement the older Petter PH and PJ range, not to replace them.

Among the many key Petter staff alternating between Staines and Dursley was David Mayne. David was another Staines ex-apprentice with over forty years service in Petters' technical sales. He eventually moved to Dursley and is now Lister-Petter's parts marketing manager in addition to being responsible for all their exhibition participation and sales literature.

A committee of technicians and sales staff, chaired by John Stevens, was set up to explore the parameters for future engines. The Staines R&D Centre and also the Ironbarks works closed for site redevelopment as a science park industrial estate; the Causeway factory remained open for some months making A series

The Lagonda trolley used to move machined components in Causeway factory, Staines, from
c. 1920 until 1987; the wheels are from the rare 11.1 hp Lagonda model 'K'

engines, including the twin-cylinder version of the AD. Production of Petters'
PH and PJ engines ceased. Evenually, the Causeway works also closed for site
redevelopment; it is now a Sainsbury supermarket and a small plaque in the
building states that it is built on the site of the Lagonda car works.

During the initial integration of Staines personnel into Dursley, the managing
director there was David Esse. Tragically he was not to see the final result for he
died after a short illness in 1985. Richard Lister, sales and marketing director,
assumed the responsibilities of the MD for a short period before Stan Keyworth,
ex-managing director of Dorman Diesels, took over.

An historic meeting took place in the Priory at Dursley in 1985 when a large
gathering of technical and sales staff of both companies met to hear the findings
of a Hawker Siddeley world survey into the future requirements for engines up
to 70 hp. The survey was conducted by METRA with its findings leading to the
design and development of project LP460, now known as the Alpha range.
Design work started on the Alpha engines in May 1985.

The new firm of Lister-Petter Ltd was formed on 1 January 1986 under the
managing directorship of Stan Keyworth. The Petter aluminium AC1 and AD1

engines introduced in the seventies and eighties continued to be produced by Lister-Petter Ltd, along with selected models from the R.A. Lister range.

So Listers and Petters were wed after an engagement that commenced in 1965 with Lister's acquisition by Hawker Siddeley Group. However, the relationship went back much earlier, to 1897, when the two companies had exhibited and marketed each other's products. They continued to trade with each other until 1908, when R.A. Lister & Co. began to make petrol engines, and so the two companies became competitors for almost eighty years. Now Lister and Petter are under one name and one roof heading for the twenty-first century.

Despite being formed at one of the most crucial trading times in the last one hundred years, Lister-Petter continued to flourish despite the increasingly depressed construction industry which for many years had been the mainstay of their joint engine sales. Now the latest Alpha engines, designed to meet the needs of that tough industry, are leading the way and the company was more than satisfied when they received gold and silver medals from *Contract Journal*, the organizers of the SED (Site Equipment Demonstration) where the Alpha range was launched in April 1988. Following the success of the industrial Alpha engines, the company marinized these 20, 30 and 40 hp diesels to bring their technology to the benefit of the marine world. The Alpha engines were the first

The Lister-Petter Alpha range of diesel engines

products of the combined resources of Lister and Petter technicians, the expertise of which is reflected in the compact, efficient power units.

Gerald Howell, ex-Westinghouse, became managing director of Lister-Petter Ltd in October 1988. As the decade changed so too did the Lister-Petter parentage.

The Hawker Siddeley Group, comprising over one hundred and forty companies, was acquired by the BTR Group in 1991. The new managing director of Lister-Petter became ex-production director, Terry Sharpe, and the company took on a new look as part of BTR's giant international industrial engineering investment. BTR were able to provide the valuable management and structured financial resources Lister-Petter needed to take it towards the year 2000 in the forefront of diesel technology.

Historical footnote: Westland Aircraft Co. Ltd, created by Petters in 1915, started to make Sikorski helicopters under licence in 1948. They acquired the Saunders-Roe helicopter division in 1960, followed by the helicopter divisions of Bristol Aircraft and Fairey Aviation. Westland Helicopters Ltd were themselves acquired by GKN Group on 30 March 1994. The purchase by a British industrial company brought to an end a saga that had forced the resignation of a cabinet minister over fears that a foreign helicopter manufacturer would acquire Westland; a situation that took until July 1995 to resolve when the company received an order for sixty-seven McDonnell Douglas Apache Attack Helicopters from the British army, valued at £2.5 billion.

1895–1939

Petter Engines

DISCOURSE AND DATA

When the Petter twins, Ernest and Percy, aided by their elder brother Guy and foundry foreman Ben Jacobs, made their first oil engine in 1895, they could not have envisaged the nonstop production of power units that was to follow for the next one hundred years. Although the company was never to see the fulfilment of the twins' ambition to enter long-term automotive manufacture, it did produce a very wide range of engines operating on many different fuels and for an infinite list of applications. Many Petter engines were unique in their design for, if nothing else, the company was always at the forefront of development, a position confirmed by their enviable list of patents and awards. The following specifications and operating data lists all Petter engines and, where possible, identifies the date of introduction and end of production. By virtue of space, it is not practical to quote all modifications or upratings, as these were implemented by the company on a continuous programme of improvement.

1893 – Horizontal, single-acting, single-cylinder steam engine designed by Ben Jacobs and rated at $1\frac{3}{4}$ hp @ 300 r/min. Lubrication by greaser to bearings with wick oil feed to the piston. Probably used for operating water pumps, winnowing and root pulping. The company museum had the only known example in 1972.

1895 – Horizontal, single-cylinder, water-cooled, four-stroke oil engine of 1 hp @ 350 r/min. Probably designed as the smallest of a range of stationary engines for agricultural purposes. Illustrated in *The Engineer*, 3 April 1896, in the review of Petters' horseless carriage powered by a modified version of this engine.

The automotive version had two parallel steel bars to carry the main bearings in place of the traditional cast-iron bed of the stationary models. The crankshaft was balanced and had a bored recess in which was carried sufficient oil for a day's operation. When the starting handle was placed in position, it opened the exhaust valve, so acting as a decompressor. The heavy, large-diameter, spoked flywheel of the stationary version was replaced with a smaller diameter flywheel.

Gravity-fed fuel oil entered the combustion chamber via the air valve. The exhaust valve was actuated by spur-wheels and cam-driven by the crankshaft. The inlet valve was opened by suction from the descending piston. Both valves could be removed for cleaning and replacement within two minutes. Ignition: hot-tube heated by exterior positioned lamp. Piston size: 3.5 in; stroke 6 in; weight 120 lb. Presented to the Yeovil Museum.

1896 – Petter Patent Petroleum Oil Engines. These horizontal, single-cylinder, water-cooled, four-stroke engines were designed and first exhibited at the Somerset Show, 1896; they were later referred to as the Standard range to differentiate between the 1903 Handyman series that looked very similar.

1897 – (May). Horizontal, side-by-side twin-cylinder, water-cooled, four-stroke of 3 hp @ 350 r/min. Described by *The Engineer* of 4 June 1897 in a review of entrants in their motor vehicle competition at Crystal Palace on 31 May 1897. The engine was described as a Petter Patent Petroleum Oil Engine operating on Royal Daylight fuel with twin ignition tubes heated by a single blowlamp. The exhaust valves were operated by levers, chain-driven from the crankshaft.

1897 – (July). Petter Patent Petroleum Oil Engines. Horizontal, single-cylinder, water-cooled, four-stroke engines of 1 hp, 2.5 hp and 5 hp exhibited at the Royal Show.

1899 – (July). Petter Patent Petroleum Portable Oil Engine. Horizontal, single-cylinder, water-cooled, 1¼ hp @ 350 r/min. Introduced at the Royal Show, Maidstone. This portable engine was mounted on a four-wheel trolley with draught handle and a large cylindrical, corrugated water-cooling tank situated in front of the engine. Other unspecified engines of larger size were exhibited, including one coupled to a water pump.

1900 – By this time some 2,000 Standard Petter Patent Petroleum Oil Engines had been made in ten sizes ranging from 1¼ to 30 hp. Consisting of 1¼, 2.5, 3.5, 5, 6, 8, 12½, 17, 21 and 30 hp versions, they were phased out in 1915. Water injection had been added on all units over 3 hp to increase performance. By 1901 the engines were fitted with exhaust-heated lampless tube ignition and centrifugal ball governors giving proportionate fuel/air control. They were marketed as the ideal power source for farmers, being strong, reliable and having no fire hazard.

The crankshafts were cut from a solid block of steel and the journals ground to an unusually large diameter. The gun-metal bearings had provision for wear adjustment. The engines were painted in four coats of mid-Brunswick Green, gold-lined around the perimeter of the bed-plate and cylinder and finished with a coat of clear varnish. The bed-plate castings carried the words 'Petter Yeovil England' in raised lettering. Portable versions of 1¼ to 17 hp were available mounted on four-wheel trolleys or trailers, depending on the engine size. The combined engine/pump sets ranged from 1¼ hp to 3 hp and were capable of pumping from 500 to 2,500 gph at 120 ft total head. It was claimed that Petters were the first to introduce combination pump sets; they were also experimenting with oil-engined agricultural tractors in 1900.

1902 – Portable, self-propelled oil engine. Single-cylinder, water-cooled 5 hp @ 380 r/min. Piston, 7¼ in diameter, stroke, 9¾ in. A 28 gallon water tank mounted in front of the engine contained cooling water that was sprayed by a rotary pump on to baffle plates in the chimney where the upward current of air cooled it. Lubrication was by total loss oil with capacity for 12 hours' operation being carried. This was the first new product to be introduced by the revised company of James B. Petter and Sons Ltd.

1903 – Experimental oil engine-powered agricultural tractor exhibited at RASE Show, Park Royal.

1903 – The Handyman agricultural series introduced and awarded silver medal at Staffordshire Agricultural Show. Similar in design to the Standard range, the Handyman was lighter in construction and fitted with patented lampless tube ignition, proportionate governing, bent-steel crankshaft and twin flywheels. The Handyman horizontal, single-cylinder, water-cooled, four-stroke engines were made in 1½, 2¼ and 3½ hp, and usually supplied mounted on a draught handled, four-wheeled trolley complete with water tank. The larger 5, 8 and 10 hp models were usually supplied on a horse-drawn trailer. The Handyman Series were:

Model	Power rating			Weight	Price
HAF	1½ hp	@	450 rpm	504 lb	£32
HF	2¼ hp	@	450 rpm	560 lb	£36
HB	3½ hp	@	400 rpm	1,176 lb	£48
H3M	7 hp	@	400 rpm	1,400 lb	£60
HC	8 hp	@	320 rpm	2,968 lb	£85
HD	10 hp	@	300 rpm	3,584 lb	£100

The Handyman series was also offered with combinations of grinding mills, chaff cutters, root pulpers, cake mills and saw benches. The circular saw size ranged from 14 in diameter for the 1¼ hp to 30 in diameter for the 10 hp.

1911 – By this time the company had produced over 5,000 engines of the Standard and Handyman series. The Standard range now consisted of eleven models, including AF 1½ hp, FF 2¼ hp, BB 3½ hp, MM 6 hp, CC 8 hp, DD 10 hp, KK 15 hp, GG 20 hp, EE 26 hp, JJ 38 hp and LL 50 hp. They were equipped with adjustable inlet valves to permit a wide choice of low-grade fuels. The engines of 15 hp and above had forced-feed lubrication to cylinders and ring lubricators on the crankshafts. Their prices ranged from the AF at £40 to the LL at £485. The Standard Series included:

Model	Power rating			Flywheel	Weight
AF	1½–2¼ hp	@	450 rpm	24 in	672 lb
FF	2¼–3 hp	@	450 rpm	24 in	784 lb
BB	3½–5 hp	@	350 rpm	36 in	1,680 lb
MM	6–7½ hp	@	330 rpm	42 in	2,016 lb
CC	8–10 hp	@	270 rpm	44 in	3,136 lb
DD	10–12½ hp	@	250 rpm	48 in	3,584 lb
KK	15–18 hp	@	230 rpm	54 in	6,272 lb
GG	20–24 hp	@	230 rpm	54 in	5,936 lb
EE	26–32 hp	@	230 rpm	54 in	9,408 lb
JJ	38–45 hp	@	225 rpm	60 in	12,656 lb
LL	50–60 hp	@	210 rpm	84 in	20,048 lb

The Portable Models included:

Model		Length	Weight	Price
P2B	3½ hp	8ft	3,360 lb	£90
P2M	6 hp	8 ft 3 in	3,472 lb	£120
P2C	8½ hp	11 ft	5,376 lb	£152
P2D	11½ hp	11 ft	5,936 lb	£174
P2K	15½ hp	11 ft	7,728 lb	£220
P2G	20 hp	12 ft 6 in	8,400 lb	£235

The Standard range were also sold with a variety of equipment forming combination sets. These included: direct-coupled and belt-driven dynamos from 1,000 W to 25,000 W; Stella lighting sets from 500 W to 3,000 W; combination water pumps from 500 to 2,500 gph at 150 ft; twin water pumps from 2,440 to 35,240 gph; sewerage centrifugal pumps from 80 to 4,000 gph; deep-well pumps of 50 ft to 200 ft; vertical Triplex power pumps from 300 to 600 ft head.

The Standard 30 hp engine was modified for installation in Petters' own traction engine, introduced in 1911 for haulage and threshing. The engine had a piston diameter of 10¾ in and a stroke of 12 in; it was equipped with sufficient fuel and water for 10 hours' operation, including a hauling capacity of 8 ton loads on normal roads. The crankshaft was contained in a dust-proof crankcase. The tractor had forward and reverse speeds of $2\frac{1}{2}$ or 5 mph and a power-take-off pulley. The radiator consisted of 180 ft of wound copper tubing under discs and gills, with a flat-bladed fan inside the coil for additional cooling.

1911 – Petters started to produce two-stroke crude oil engines, known as Semi-Diesels, ranging from 8 to 200 hp. The Semi-Diesels were awarded a gold medal at the Turin International Exhibition in 1911. The Semi-Diesels later became the S type and later still the Surface Ignition engines. These were vertical, single- and multi-cylinder, water-cooled, low compression engines with lamp-assisted starting. They had removable water-cooled cylinder heads and a water-jacketed cylinder, both fed by a circulating pump. The crankshaft was cut from a solid block of Siemens Martin Open Hearth steel. The engines were painted in two coats of lead primer only.

The S type had excellent low fuel consumption and the ability to operate on very low-grade fuel oil. Typical fuels were Russian Naphtha, Scotch Shale or, with slightly less power, residual oils such as Texas, Resoleum and Admiralty fuel oil.

The S models included:

	VC	VD	VK	VG	VE	VJ	VN
bhp	8	10	16	25	35	50	70
rpm	375	350	325	300	275	250	225
P. Dia.	$7\frac{1}{4}$ in	$8\frac{1}{4}$ in	$9\frac{3}{4}$ in	$10\frac{3}{4}$ in	12 in	14 in	16 in
Stroke	8 in	9 in	$0\frac{1}{2}$ in	$11\frac{1}{2}$ in	14 in	16 in	18 in
F. Dia.	42 in	48 in	54 in	60 in	72 in	78 in	84 in
Wt. cwt	24	31	42	61	96	126	175
Price £	131	163	202	252	315	394	551

	VE2	VJ2	VE3	VE4	VJ3	VJ4
bhp	70	100	105	140	150	200
r/min	275	250	275	320	250	285
No. of cyl.	2	2	3	4	3	4
P. Dia.	12 in	14 in	12 in	12 in	14 in	14 in
Stroke	14 in	16 in	14 in	12 in	16 in	14 in
F. Dia.	66 in	72 in	66 in	66 in	72 in	72 in
Wt. cwt	160	210	224	260	294	348
Price £	615	761	915	1,188	1,130	1,470

In 1916 the VN2 140 hp and the VN4 280 hp were added to the S range.

1916 – The total number of Petter engines made reached 12,000.

1916 – The Universal was introduced. A 5 hp vertical, single-cylinder, water-cooled, two-stroke engine that started on petrol and automatically switched to paraffin for working, drawing fuel oil from the base tank via a patented fuel pump. The magneto ignition system gave instant starting without pre-heating. The Universal later became the Petter Junior series of 1½, 3, 5 and 8 hp engines and could be ordered for petrol, benzol, alcohol or town gas operation, depending on customer preference and local fuel costs. A range of special cylinder heads was available to achieve the best operation from this wide choice of fuels. Oil bath bearings were fitted to all Junior models except the 1½ hp Little Pet, which was introduced in 1922. Originally intended to operate on petrol only, the Little Pet was sold for paraffin operation where no 'light-load' running was envisaged. Instead of oil bath bearings like the other Junior models, the Little Pet was equipped with grease lubrication to the main bearings and oil to the large and small ends, cylinder and piston.

The Little Pet also had a distinctive water-hopper that was cast integral with the cylinder.

	Bhp	*rpm*	*Flywheel*	*Saw size*	*Price*
Little Pet	1½	750	16 in	nil	£30
Junior	3	700	17 in	18 in	£37 10s
Junior	5	600	22 in	24 in	£62
Junior	8	550	26 in	30 in	£108

The Junior 3 hp engine with ride-on 12½ cwt lawn/road roller was also available at £125.

The Junior series was also offered with a wide range of direct coupled air compressors, electrical plants, dynamos, pump and combination sets.

1917 – Two Junior models, the 6 and 10 hp versions, were offered as marine propulsion units. These were supplied with the engine and gearbox mounted on a common baseplate.

1917 – The Standard range of horizontal engines of 9 hp to 25 hp ceased production. The S industrial range of 9 hp to 300 hp were also offered as direct reversing marine propulsion units. The production of small engines moved from the Nautilus works to the Westland works.

1917 – The Westland Plough works opened for the manufacture of Petter engined ploughs and tractors.

1918 – Manufacture of engines over 25 hp moved to Ipswich with the formation of Vickers-Petters Ltd. Total number of Petter engines made reached 14,255. The S range improved by a patented crankshaft-driven governor controlling quantity of fuel and moment of ignition in relation to load, so overcoming previous problems of light-load operation.

1923 – The total number of Petter engines made exceeded 30,000. The Junior range became the M type. The Petter motor roller was discontinued. The cold-starter cartridge on the S type received an RASE silver medal. The S range restricted to 5, 8, 12–14 and 18–21 hp vertical singles, 24–28 and 36–42 hp twins. They could also be purchased in horizontal form as 8–9, 12–14 and 18–21 hp models in stationary or portable form.

1924 – The Vickers-Petter range of ten heavy oil engines were from 50 to 510 hp and primarily for marine propulsion and auxiliary applications or civil engineering water and sewage pumping. The two-cylinder marine model could be supplied with a gearbox or automatic reverse rotation.

The four- and six-cylinder Vickers-Petter marine engines used compressed air to actuate reverse operation. A new type of cold-starting lamp allowed start-up in one minute, while a special light-load device permitted prolonged slow-speed operation at quarter throttle without additional heating lamps.

The Vickers-Petter Heavy Oil Engines included:

	H2M	L2M	M2M	R2M	H4M	L4M	M4M	R4M	S4M	S6M
Max. bhp	50	60	90	120	100	120	180	240	340	510
rpm	375	325	300	275	327	325	300	275	250	250
Wt. cwt	70	100	135	210	130	200	230	280	400	540

1924 – M type revised to $1\frac{1}{2}$, 3 and 5 hp, with a number of Petter-Light sets being manufactured using the M type to produce $\frac{3}{4}$ kW to $2\frac{1}{4}$ kW.

1930 – Petters reach 100,000 engines and produce the Atomic range. The Atomics were vertical, high-compression, airless-injection, two-stroke, cold-starting oil engines with a crankshaft-driven, variable-speed governor. They were designed to operate on a wide range of cheap fuels with extremely low consumption. Removal of the cylinder could take place without disturbing the crankshaft sealing rings. The patented Petter calibrater system supplied the lubrication, and these were the first engines to be so equipped.

Made at the Westland works, the Atomics were available in the following specifications:

	TT	TU	TV	TV2	TX	TW2	TY	TX2	TZ	TX3
bhp	5	8	15	30	36	50	56	72	90	108
rpm	750	650	625	625	500	590	410	500	330	500
No. of cyl.	1	1	1	2	1	2	1	2	1	3
Wt. cwt	6	11	19	38	52	60	88	73	154	89

	TY2	TX4	TY3	TZ2	TY4	TZ3	TZ4	TZ5	TZ6
bhp	112	144	168	180	224	270	360	450	540
rpm	410	500	410	330	410	330	330	330	330
No. of cyl.	2	4	3	2	4	3	4	5	6
Wt. cwt	122	112	164	215	196	283	375	430	508

Marine Atomics consisted of: two cyl. 50 hp; three cyl. 75 hp, 120 hp, and 195 hp; four cyl. 100 hp, 160 hp and 260 hp; six cyl. 400 hp. The Petter Universal continued in 1½, 2, 3 and 5 hp stationary, semi-portable and portable form.

1930 – The Petter S types were produced in 5–36 hp for stationary and marine use, with a special lightweight 18/20 hp version for combination and lighting units, weighing 16.5 cwt instead of 36 cwt. They were also available as portable models of 5, 8, 12/14 and 18/21 hp.

1932 – The new Universal Air Cooled Petrol Engine was introduced. This horizontally opposed 170 lb engine became the workhorse of the armed services in the Second World War, with many different applications in all theatres of war.

The Universal became known as the PU series in single and twin form of 2 hp to 8 hp. Its original market had been construction applications in civil engineering; there was also a marine version for small inshore boats that could go from full ahead to full astern in 4 seconds. The single sold for £22 and the twin £33.

The Universal was the first Petter engine to offer drive at crankshaft (1,500 r/min) and camshaft (750 r/min), an option later to be adopted on all postwar engines. Air cooling was by a centrifugal, flywheel-mounted fan and lubrication was provided by a forced-feed plunger-type pump. The over engine-mounted fuel tank held sufficient supply for a day's operation, as consumption from the Zenith carburettor was ¾ pt per hour on full power. Ignition was provided by a British Thompson-Houston high-tension magneto. The engines could be ordered in left- or right-hand rotation.

1932 – The Petter High Speed Compression Ignition ACE Atomics of 16–60 hp were no relation to the previous Atomic range. These compact diesels were designed with independent air scavenge pumps to each cylinder, the capacity of the pumps exceeding that of the power cylinders they supplied.

The ACE Atomics were designed primarily for automotive and traction applications, operating at 250 to 1,600 r/min with optimum power being reached at 1,000 r/min. They were made in three- and four-cylinder specifications only, and weighed 11½ cwt and 15 cwt respectively. Although they appeared to operate very well in testbed shunting, their manufacture was short-lived but probably led Petters into the development of the Super Scavenge, otherwise known as SS, engines.

1936 – The Petter Harmonic Induction Engine. This vertical, single-cylinder, water-cooled two-stroke was a research project. The engine had a compact, column-like appearance with only the external flywheel breaking the smooth shape. Made in one size, 16 bhp @ 1,000 r/min, it relied on a tuned exhaust system to produce a scavenge method of combustion without pumps or blowers. Approximately one hundred were made.

1936 – The S type was restricted to four models: 6, 10, 15 and 21 hp.

1937 – The Atomic range was increased by the addition of the TTS 6 hp, the TUS 10 hp @ 900 r/min and the TUS2 20 hp @ 800 r/min.

1938 – The Petter SS or Super Scavenge two-stroke diesel was introduced. Primarily intended for general industrial applications, marine propulsion and automotive traction, this range of five engines had a crankshaft-driven blower providing a unidirectional scavenge system with additional overhead exhaust valve.

There was special water-cooling around the copper-sheathed atomizer and the exhaust ports. The SS range included:

	SS2	SS3	SS4	SS5	SS6
bhp	125	187	250	312	375
rpm	500	500	500	500	500
Bore	8½ in	8½ in	8½ in	8½ in	8½ in
Stroke	13 in	13 in	13 in	13 in	13 in
Wt. cwt	85	105	125	149	162

1938 – Petter Type A Air-cooled Petrol Engine. This vertical, single-cylinder power unit was introduced for the civil engineering market and agriculture where, in its petrol or paraffin form, it found wide acceptance as a reliable workhorse. The engine was also extensively used in applications designed for the armed forces. The A type was produced in 1½, 2 and 3 hp versions with drive from the full-speed crankshaft position only. The A type petrol engine had high-tension magneto ignition with impulse starter for fatter spark. Cooling air was supplied from the flywheel-mounted fan and lubrication was by the trouble-free splash method. The carburettor was Petters' own design using a variable jet and a patent strangler for easy starting. An integral 1¼ gallon tank was mounted over the engine. The centrifugal governor allowed a 20 per cent speed variation while the engine was running. The engine was produced until the series II came out in 1946. The three models in this range were:

	A	A	AS
bhp	$1\frac{1}{2}$	2	3
r/min petrol	750	1,000	1,500
r/min paraffin	850	1,000	1,500
weight (lb)	172	172	172
Price petrol	£19 10*s*	£19 10*s*	£21 15*s*
Price paraffin	£20 0*s*	£20 0*s*	£22 5*s*

1939 – The S type was dropped; the Atomics produced in 5 to 20 hp only; the SS made to 375 bhp. The A and PU series continued with a $2\frac{1}{2}$ hp version and an M type was used to power a $2\frac{1}{2}$ kW generating set.

1940–86

Petter Engines

DISCOURSE AND DATA

During the Second World War, Petters continued to manufacture the A and PU series of air-cooled petrol engines as well as producing a significant amount of tank munitions. In the years immediately after the war, many thousands of A series engines were built by McLarens under subcontract from Petters, pending the company's move to Staines. The SS range continued, in part, until 1951.

McLaren's Airedale works at Leeds continued making Petter-Fielding DH1, EH1 and FH1/2 horizontal oil engines of 16/21 hp, 27 bhp @ 800 r/min and 40/80 bhp at 500/650 r/min mainly for the Middle East market until the mid-fifties.

1946 – The A series II petrol engines were introduced and continued to be manufactured, in part, until the late seventies.

1947 – The first major postwar development in Petters' industrial diesel engines was the introduction of the AV Series I range. These were vertical, water-cooled, four-stroke engines produced by Associated British Oil Engines Ltd, of which Petters were a member company. These monobloc, cast-iron power units ranged from 3 to 10 bhp @ 1,000 to 1,500 r/min and were made in single and twin form. The AV had a bore of 80 mm and a stroke of 110 mm with a combustion chamber of the 'Cub' design. Wet liners were fitted to the cylinders and drive could be taken from full-speed crankshaft or half-speed camshaft positions at the gear-end or full-speed at the flywheel end.

The engines were equipped with Bryce Berger fuel injection equipment, for that company was also part of the Brush Group and occupied an adjacent factory to Petters' Causeway works where the AVs were produced.

1950 – The AVA Series I, the air-cooled version of the AV, was introduced. With the marine versions of both engines these became the best-selling diesels the company had ever produced.

1951 – SS production ceased.

1952 – The A series, water-cooled W1, W1H and W1HP introduced; these were petrol and vaporizing oil engines of 1 to 2 bhp, the latter two with water-hopper cooling. The PA1 and PA2, air-cooled, petrol engines were introduced to extend the A series, together with their water-cooled versions. These engines were rated from 3 to 10 bhp @ 1,150 to 1,800 r/min.

The PAK, a vaporizing oil version in single- and twin-cylinder specification, was also available as an air compressor, as were the PA2 and PA2W engines. The compressor versions were marketed as PA2C and PA2CW units producing 100 psi continuous or 350 psi intermittent @ 1,000 r/min.

1952 – The B type water-cooled diesels introduced. Designed and developed at Loughborough, they were made in two-, three- and four-cylinder specification and made particularly good marine propulsion units, producing 13 to 40 bhp @ 1,000 to 1,500 r/min. A traction version of 14.25 to 44 bhp was also made. In 1955, the B types were passed to McLarens at Leeds for manufacture with the prototypes of the PD/PDV air-cooled diesels, restricting Petters once again to 20 bhp.

1953 – The AV/AVA Series II introduced; phased out 1967.

1954 – Top of the PA range introduced as the PAV4 and PAV4K. These air-cooled petrol and vaporizing oil engines were rated at 13.5 to 17.5 bhp @ 1,400 to 2,000 r/min.

1954 – The famous PAZ1 announced. One of the most loved and longlived engines from Petters. The PAZ1 and its later companion, the PAZ1 Compact, were the backbone of the small cement mixer and water-pump market in post-war Britain. The PAZ1 was a vertical, single-cylinder, air-cooled diesel of $1\frac{1}{2}$ to $2\frac{1}{2}$ bhp @ 1,000 and 1,500 r/min. It later became a firm favourite with African and Far East markets where it was used extensively to drive rice hullers and root cutters, etc. The engine was so respected overseas that Petters produced the AC1ZS, a version of their lightweight, high-speed, A range of diesels in the late seventies when the original PAZ1 was phased out.

1956 – The PH/PHW single and twins introduced. These were very similar to the AV/AVA engines, with performance increased to 4 to 15 bhp @ 1,000 to 1,800 r/min.

1957 – The Brush Group acquired by Hawker Siddeley. Petters become part of Hawker Siddeley Diesels. The PC range of multi-cylinder, high-speed, air-cooled diesels introduced for automotive applications and marine use. Prototypes installed at London's Heathrow airport powering aircraft towing-trucks and runabouts. The range were made in one- to four-cylinder specification and produced $3\frac{1}{4}$ to 20 bhp @ 2,000 to 3,000 r/min.

The company were now manufacturing an impressive range of fifty-one different engines for industrial and marine applications. They included PAZ1, AV/AVAs, PH/PHWs, PC1, 2, 3, 4, A1, PA1/2 and PAV4, AP1, PA1/2K, PAV4K, and the marine versions of AV/AVAs, PH/PHWs, and PC2, 3, 4.

1960 – The production of PD/PDV and B type engines returned to Staines, taking Petters' horsepower from $1\frac{1}{2}$ to 108 bhp in the air-cooled range and 3 to 48 bhp in water-cooled. Vaporizing oil engines of $1\frac{1}{2}$ to 10 bhp were also manufactured. The PDs were vertical, air-cooled engines of two, three, four, V six and V eight cylinders of 16 to 108 bhp @ 1,200 to 2,000 r/min.

1960 – The PA1, PA2 and PA2C discontinued.

1962 – The B type replaced by the PJ/PJW range of air- and water-cooled, single- and twin-cylinder diesels. The three- and four-cylinder versions of the PJ/PJW were added in 1963, taking the range from 5 to 45 bhp at 1,000 to 2,000 r/min. The PJ range owed its development to the AV and PH engines, for they represented a logical progression over sixteen years. The increased power was achieved by increasing the bore and bmep while maintaining the stroke. The piston design was improved by adding a toroidal bowl and the cylinder head through-bolted to the crankcase to contain the additional power. Fifty prototypes were built for endurance and field testing and totalled 25,500 hours running. The air-cooled models were equipped with flywheel-mounted fans on the single and twins, while the three- and four-cylinder models had vee-belt-driven axial fans. PJ engines departed from the mid-Brunswick Green of all Petter engines, being finished in a lighter metallic shade of green.

1964 – Petters announced an entirely new concept in small, lightweight, high-speed, air-cooled diesel engines. The AA1 was a 1.5 to 3.5 bhp @ 1,500 to 3,600 r/min engine constructed mainly of die-cast aluminium and weighing only 95 lb.

The AA1 was marketed for several years as the smallest air-cooled diesel in the world and won for Petters a Queen's Award to Industry in 1966 for 'technological innovation in diesel engine design'. The AA1 used the famous Lanova air cell type of combustion chamber, producing good starting, power output and low fuel consumption. The engine required priming in cold weather by the unusual use of the dip-stick and lubricating oil being dripped into a priming port on top of the rocker box. A nylon fan, mounted on the flywheel, supplied the air cooling and was contained in an integral bellhousing.

1967 – The AB1 introduced. This natural development from the AA1 produced 2.3 to 5 bhp @ 1,500 to 3,600 r/min for the same overall size and weight. Using a higher bmep, the AB1 had an increased bore to achieve the extra power. The obvious visual difference between it and the AA1 was a slightly larger fuel tank. The DA1 and BA1 air-cooled diesels were announced. These lightweight, high-speed engines were also of aluminium construction and represented the growth of development from Petters' design team following six years of intensive work in the company's R&D Centre.

The new family of BA engines resulted from market surveys of the construction industry which revealed a continuing demand for small diesel power units of ever-decreasing size and weight with higher operating speeds. The DA and BA engines were designed for continuous operation at 3,000 r/min producing 6.5 and 10 bhp respectively. Being able to operate continuously at 3,000 r/min enabled them to be direct coupled, via their integral sae bellhousing, to electrical generating and welding sets. Both engines had a permanently engaged hand-starting dog within a protective housing, and an automatic decompressor with plunger-type oil priming for cold-weather starting.

The A and B series of lightweight engines had interchangeable gear covers for optional gear reduction if required. Drive could be taken from the flywheel or gear-end with full-speed crankshaft and half-speed camshaft drive at the gear-end. When power was taken from the gear-end, hand-starting was transferred to the flywheel end via a plate attachment to the bellhousing carrying a slow-speed gear.

1970 – The DA1 was discontinued as the AC1, developed from the AA1, produced 2.8 to 6.5 bhp at the same speeds for a smaller overall size.

1970 – The BA2, a twin-cylinder version of the BA1, producing 13.5 to 20 bhp @ 1,800 to 3,000 r/min, introduced. The water-cooled marine version of the AB1 also made its debut as the AB1WRMR of 5 bhp @ 3,000 r/min.

1972 – The Petter Jumbo-weight PHW and PJW water-cooled engines were specially produced for the African market. These 6.3 and 8.5 bhp @ 1,500 r/min twin-flywheel versions of the standard marques were introduced for grain-milling and water-pumping applications where twin flywheel engines had always been used and were respected.

1972 – The PK3, an uprated version of the PJ3, announced. This air-cooled, three-cylinder engine produced 46 bhp @ 2,000 r/min and was fitted with aluminium cylinder heads.

1978 – The award-winning Petter AC2, vertical, twin-cylinder, air-cooled diesel introduced. Petters received a Premier Design Council Award for this engine in 1979. Rated at 9 to 12 bhp @ 2,500 to 3,600 r/min, the AC2 found many applications in the electrical generating and welding set market together with various types of hydraulic and high-pressure water-pumps.

1979 – The introduction of the AC1ZS, the new PAZ1 as it was sometimes called. Two models were made: the 805 of 1.6 to 2.2 bhp @ 1,000/1,250 r/min and the 806 of 2.2 to 3.3 bhp @ 1,250/1,800 r/min. The water-cooled version of the AC2 announced in industrial form for generating-sets and as a marine propulsion unit of 12 bhp.

1982 – The PJ1Z and PJ2Z in air- and water-cooled forms introduced. Rated at 5 to 22.5 bhp @ 1,000 to 2,000 r/min. The AC1Z re-rated at 2.3 to 3,000 bhp with variable speed between 1,500 and 3,000 r/min. The AC1ZS, rated at 1.5 to 3 bhp @ 1,000 to 1,800 r/min.

1983 – The A range of diesels increased again by the announcement of the AD1 of 2.5 to 5.6 bhp @ 1,500 to 3,600 r/min. The twin-cylinder version, AD2 of 5 to 11.2 bhp @ 1,500 to 3,600 r/min, was introduced in 1984 but was phased out shortly after the merger of Lister and Petters.

1984 – The P600 range of vertical, two- and three-cylinder air-cooled diesels of 14 to 37.5 bhp at 1,500 to 3,000 r/min. Developed from the PK3, this new range was available in a number of models to suit various applications. The 1,500/1,800 r/min models of the P600 were for generating sets of 50 and 60 Hz; the engine was also ideal for 3 ton dumpers, taking Petters beyond their previous 2½ ton maximum. One-piece gravity die-cast aluminium cylinder heads, with cross-flow ports, allowed the inlet valves to be positioned on the cool side of the engine. The helical inlet ports gave high swirl and low restriction, and with the toroidal piston bowl gave good combustion with low noise and emission. The P600s were designed to power hydraulic pumps from any of three positions or all at the same time, and could also be fitted with bolt-on hydraulic pumps at either end of the crankshaft.

The P600 was the last engine to enter service under the company's name before Petters were merged with R.A. Lister Ltd to form Lister-Petter Ltd in 1986; it was also the first joint venture design produced by the two companies before merger and shared a common crankcase and crankshaft with the Lister TL. The P600 used a gear-pump for oil lubrication whereas the TL used a plunger pump.

1988 – The Alpha range of 20, 30 and 40 hp engines were introduced, followed by their marine versions. They were the first engines to be marketed by Lister-Petter Ltd, from the combined works at Dursley.

All bhp quoted in this Appendix are continuous 'A' ratings, a practice that Petters used until competition forced them to market engines at their intermittent 'B' ratings from 1979.

Historical Petter Dates

1821	Birth of John Petter Junior
1823	Birth of Eliza Bazeley (John's wife)
1847	Birth of James Bazeley Petter (founder of Petters)
	Birth of Charlotte W. Branscombe (James's wife)
1852	John and Edwin Petter establish North Devon Foundry
1865	John Petter and family move to Yeovil
	John Petter buys ironmongery (Josiah Hanham)
1868	James B. Petter marries Charlotte W. Branscombe
1871	James made manager of ironmongers shop
1872	Birth of Harry Petter (James H.B.) (James's first son)
	James B. Petter buys Yeovil Iron & Brass Foundry
	Birth of Guy B. Petter (second son)
	John Petter trading as manufacturer and ironmonger
1873	Birth of the twins Ernest and Percival (third and fourth sons)
1874	Birth of Hugh Petter (fifth son)
1875	Birth of Mary Petter (James's first daughter)
1876	Birth of Gertrude Petter (second daughter)
1879	Birth of John Petter (sixth son – architect)
	Brush Electrical Engineering Co. established
1881	Birth of Claude A. Petter (seventh son)
	James B. Petter invents the Nautilus grate
	The opening of the first Nautilus grate works
1883	Birth of Richard C. Petter (Capt. Dick)
1886	Birth of Eliza (third daughter)
1886	James B. Petter takes over his father's ironmongery
1887	John Petter retires
1888	Henry J. Edgar killed in trap accident
1889	Ernest and Percy Petter start work for father
1890	Birth of Evelyn B. Petter (fourth daughter)
1893	James B. Petter & Sons formed
	Ben Jacobs joins Petters
	Ben Jacobs designs Petters' first steam engine
1895	The first oil engines made by Petters
	The first Petter horseless carriage

1896	Petters' first Standard stationary engines exhibited at Somerset Show
1897	The Yeovil Motor Car & Cycle Co. formed
	Petters in Crystal Palace motor car competition
	Petters' first electric vehicle in Lord Mayor's Show
	Petters exhibit oil engines at Royal Show
1898	Petters' Bristol office opens
1899	Petters' London office opens
	Petters pump out lake for Stanley the explorer
1900	Petters' patent hot ignition tube
1901	New Nautilus Engine works opened at Reckleford
	Ernest and Percy buy engine division from James B. Petter
	James B. Petter & Sons Ltd formed
1902	Petters' first self-propelled oil engine
1903	Petter Handyman engines announced
	R.A. Lister sell Petter Handyman engines
	Petters sell Lister agricultural equipment
1905	Herbert Brookes starts apprenticeship
	Petters selling Listers' cream separator
1907	Ernest marries Angela E. Petter of Calcutta
1908	William Baines appointed to Russian sales
	Richard C. Petter joins Petters
1909	Petters sell ironmongers shop to Hill & Sawtell
1910	Petters Ltd formed
	Petters' first gold medal at Brussels International Exhibition
	Petters win Grand Prix at Turin
	Nautilus engine factory opens foundry
1911	Petters' first tractor announced
1912	William Baines becomes director
1913	Death of Rudolph Diesel on Harwich ferry
	Petters lay foundation of Westland works
	Petters receives Parliamentary Order to light Yeovil
1914	Richard Petter joins RNAS – POW in 1915
	Nautilus grates sold to Davis Gas Stove Co.
1915	Percy Petter made Yeovil town councillor
	Petters offer entire production to War Office
1916	Avro build factory at Hamble
	Petters form Westland Aircraft branch
	First Petter-Westland Short 225/184 seaplanes
1917	First Petter-Westland DH4
	Petter Iron Horse tractor announced

	First Petter–Westland-designed aircraft flies
	Nautilus Engine works at Reckleford closes
1918	Petter–Westland Vickers Vimy, the last First World War aeroplane
	First labour dispute at Westland
1919	Petters' Plough works opened at Westland site
	Petter–Westland make player pianos
	Petter–Westland make their Limousine aircraft
	Vickers–Petter Ltd formed at Ipswich
	Percy Petter takes part in Bath to London Preachers' Walk
1920	Petter–Westland win first aero prize
1921	Petters' Glasgow office opens
	Canadian Petter formed with offices in Vancouver
1924	Shell VP Petter Oil
	Ernest Petter stands as political candidate for Bristol
	Petters at British Empire Exhibition, Wembley
1925	Ernest Petter knighted
	Petter Handyman engines reintroduced
1926	Percy Petter becomes Mayor of Yeovil
	Petter–Westland Wapiti
	Petters form British Dominion Car Co. and launch Seaton–Petter car
	Vickers–Petter partnership ceases
	Petters (Ipswich) Ltd formed
	Hill–Westland Pterodactyl partnership
1927	Petter calibrater lubrication device patented
	Petter–Westland win second aero prize
	Petters Ipswich factory closes
	Petter–Westland Wapitis made in South Africa
1928	Yeovil and Petter football team reach FA Cup
1929	Petters move London office to Grosvenor Gardens
	Capt. Dick Petter appointed director
1930	Nissen–Petren barrel-shaped houses built
1931	Sir Ernest stands as Westminster candidate
1932	W.E.W. (Teddy) Petter joins the firm
1933	Petter–Westland Wallace, first flight over Everest
1934	Death of Angela E. Petter, Ernest Petter's wife
	Teddy Petter appointed technical director
	Capt. Hill resigns and Pterodactyl finishes
	Teddy Petter designs Westland Lysander
	Petter–Westland start Cierva autogyro project
	Robert A. Bruce retires as managing director of Westland branch

1935	Sir Ernest Petter marries Lucy E. Hopkins
	Westland Aircraft Ltd formed (Petter 50%)
	Moving conveyors installed at Westland works
	Petters and Westland Aircraft Ltd share Bush House, London, office
1936	Oxford University Expedition takes PU to Arctic
	Guy Petter invents adding machine
	Lt. Col. J.T.E. Moore-Brabazon joins Petters Ltd
1937	Guy Petter sells adding machine to Bell Punch Co.
	Death of Ben Jacobs, Petters' first designer
	Non-magnetic engine for Polar research ship
	Sir Ernest and Percy Petter retire
	Alan Paul Good appointed chairman of Petters Ltd
1938	Teddy Petter designs the Whirlwind aircraft
1939	Associated British Engines Ltd acquire Petter engine business
	ABE Ltd sell Westland Aircraft to John Brown Ltd
	Associated Electrical Industries take shares in Westland Aircraft Ltd
	Petters become part of Brush Engineering Co.
	Petters move to Loughborough
1940	Petters make tank turrets
1943	J. & H. McLaren acquired by ABE
1944	Mirrlees, Bickerton & Day acquired by ABE
	Teddy Petter resigns from Westland, joins English Electric, designs Canberra jet bomber
1947	ABOE (Export) sign licence with Kirloskar, which ran till 1961
	Petter-Fielding engines redesigned for McLaren to build
1948	Death of Guy B. Petter
	Petter AV engines announced
1949	Brush take over McLaren and Mirrlees
1950	Petters move to Staines
1951	Petters at Festival of Britain, London
	Herbert Brookes retires
1953	Death of A.P. Good
1954	Bryce Berger vacate Ironbarks works for Petters
	Death of Sir Ernest W. Petter
	Capt. Dick Petter becomes managing director
1955	Death of Percival W. Petter
1957	Brush Group acquired by HSI Ltd
	K. Fraser appointed managing director
1958	Petters sign agreement with Westinghouse, USA
1960	A.E. Masters appointed managing director

	Teddy Petter becomes MD of Folland Aircraft, designs Gnat jet trainer
1961	Petter Spares & Service move from Burton to Hamble
	John Dacombe retires from Service & Spares division
	Petters acquire HSI (ex-AVRO) factory at Hamble
1962	Petters' R&D Centre opens
	Petter engines built in India
1963	Petters buy Air Pumps Ltd, Raynes Park
1964	Petter AA1 announced the first aluminium engines
1965	Hawker Siddeley acquire R.A. Lister Co. Ltd
1965	Formation of Hawker Siddeley Diesels
1966	Petters receive Queen's Award to Industry for AA1
	J.D. Regis becomes director
1967	W.H. Rees appointed managing director
1968	Death of A.E. Masters
	Death of Teddy Petter
	Jim Layn appointed vice-chairman of MEEMA; chairman from 1970
1969	Sir Arnold Hall becomes chairman of Petters Ltd
1970	W.H. Rees becomes deputy chairman and managing director
	Petters marinize Volkswagen marine diesel
1972	Petter Continental BV, Rotterdam, formed
	Petters take over Mag petrol engines
1974	Death of W.H. Rees
	E.D. Dettmer, DFC, appointed managing director
1979	John Stevens appointed technical director, Petters Ltd
	COID Award for AC2 engine
	First 1,000 oil engine rally at Longleat
1980	Lister and Petter generating set divisions merge
1983	John Stevens appointed technical director of Listers and Petters
1984	T.D. Davies becomes managing director
	P600, the first combined Lister and Petter design
1985	Petters merge with R.A. Lister Co. Ltd
1986	Lister-Petter Ltd formed
1988	The first Lister-Petter Alpha engines
1989	Death of Jack Regis
1991	HSG acquired by BTR Group
	Terry Sharpe appointed managing director of Lister-Petter Ltd
1993	Death of John C. Gale
1994	Westland Aircraft Ltd acquired by GKN Group

List of Awards Received by Petters Ltd

Date	Type	Presenter
1903	Silver Medal	Staffordshire Agricultural Society
1905	Silver Medal	Royal Lancashire Agricultural Society
1907	Silver Medal	Royal Lancashire Agricultural Society
	Gold Medal	Wirral and Birkenhead Agricultural Society
	Silver Medal	Wirral and Birkenhead Agricultural Society
	Gold Medal	New Zealand Industrial Exhibition, Christchurch
	Gold & Spec.	Royal Italian Exhibition, Cologna
1908	Silver Medal	Royal Agricultural Society, Natal
	First Prize	Durban Show
	First Prize	Ladysmith Show
	Gold Medal	Padua Exhibition, Italy
	Silver Medal	Toulouse Exhibition
	Gold Medal	Faenza Exhibition, Italy
	Gold Medal	International Exhibition, Ministry of Agriculture, Piacenza
1909	Gold Medal	Pretoria, South Africa
	Silver Medal	Royal Cornwall Show
	Silver Medal	Pietermaritzburg Agricultural Show
	Diploma	Beltzi, South Russia
	Gold Medal	Rostov-on-Don, Russia
1910	Silver Medal	Ministry of Trade and Industry, St Petersburg
	Gold Medal	Brussels International Exhibition
1954	Silver Medal	Bath and West Agricultural Show
	Gold Cup	Bath and West Agricultural Show
1966	Queens Award	Department of Trade and Industry, UK
1971	Export Award	Financial Times Industrial Photography, the author and Petters Ltd
1972	Design Award	Council of Industrial Design, UK

List of Petter Patents
1881–1979

17.11.1881	J.B. Petter	Construction of fireplaces, gas and oil stoves; shaped like a shell (Nautilus)
03.08.1883	"	Oven door – insulated; provisional
27.03.1884	"	Grates – ashpans for Nautilus grates
24.05.1886	"	Increasing heat from stoves by casings of rings, chains or rods
06.05.1887	J.B.P. & W.J. Waterman	Gloves – abandoned
28.07.1887	"	Fencing posts from concave metal
03.09.1887	"	Draught control of stoves and fires
09.09.1887	"	Smoke and fire extraction chimneys for theatres
20.10.1887	"	Fireplaces, underfloor air supply
15.11.1887	"	Gas, steam and water joints – abandoned
25.04.1888	J.B. Petter	Securing panel for stove pipes through roofs
21.06.1888	"	Combined watering can/hose – abandoned
19.04.1890	"	Flu for boilers and stoves
31.10.1890	"	Oil and spirit lighting for buildings – abandoned
03.09.1891	"	Oscillating trough for cheese – abandoned
23.11.1891	"	Root-cutting machine – abandoned
25.01.1892	"	Bodkin for inserting ribbons into fabrics
14.03.1893	E.W. Petter	Fastenings for gloves – abandoned
10.07.1895	"	Ensnaring wild birds – abandoned
08.03.1895	J.B. Petter	Curd-cutter for cheese
17.04.1895	"	Easy-clean milk pails/tubs for cheese
01.05.1896	"	Opposing inlet and exhaust valves on oil engines for easier cleaning or replacement
12.07.1897	"	Opening canopies for Nautilus grates
08.11.1897	"	Drying compartment for kitchen waste fitted to stoves
27.10.1898	G.B. Petter	Cycling costumes – abandoned

17.06.1898	P.W. Petter	Vehicle brakes – abandoned
07.10.1898	"	Electric motors – abandoned
07.10.1898	"	Mowing and reaping machines – abandoned
03.04.1900	G.B. & E.W. Petter	Exhaust-heated tube ignition on oil engines
23.11.1901	E.W. Petter	Air-operated water-pump for wells
14.11.1902	J.B. Petter	Ventilating window bar – abandoned
10.09.1903	J.H. & J.B. Petter	Dustbin – abandoned
19.12.1903	"	Dustbin and sifter of ashes
13.10.1903	P.W. Petter	Cleaning and polishing machine for boots/shoes – abandoned
27.04.1904	E.W. Petter	Device for adjusting oil engine speed – abandoned
22.12.1905	J.H. & J.B. Petter	Constructing building bricks – abandoned
25.05.1906	J.B. Petter & Sons	Internal combustion engines – abandoned
25.05.1906	G.B. Petter	Internal combustion engines – abandoned
17.03.1906	J.H. & J.B. Petter	Ventilating frame for manhole covers
22.11.1907	E.W. Petter	Piston rings
14.04.1908	"	Baffle plates for fireplaces
10.11.1908	"	Fireplaces and boilers – abandoned
16.04.1908	J.H. & J.B Petter	Treating sewage – abandoned
10.03.1909	E.W. Petter	Oil engine – variable speed control via fuel needle
07.04.1909	"	Device for warming fuel oil – abandoned
01.05.1909	"	Fire grates
04.08.1910	P.W. Petter	Fuel injection on oil engines – abandoned
11.03.1911	E.W. Petter	Fuel feed to oil engines
12.06.1912	"	Internal combustion engines
24.11.1912	"	" " "
02.11.1912	"	" " "
06.12.1912	"	Regulating speed of vehicles
23.01.1913	"	" " "
28.04.1913	"	Internal combustion engines
30.08.1913	"	" " "
27.10.1913	"	Lubrication
11.11.1913	"	Internal combustion engines
11.11.1913	"	Motor car hoods
22.09.1914	"	Internal combustion engines
08.04.1914	P.W. Petter	Internal combustion engines
08.06.1914	"	" " "
07.01.1915	E.W. Petter	Tractors

29.01.1915	E.W Petter	Internal combustion engines
10.02.1915	G.B. Petter	Pumps and compressors
28.06.1915	"	" "
23.07.1915	E.W. Petter	Internal combustion engines
21.10.1915	"	Engine fuel supply
06.08.1915	G.B. Petter	Pumps and compressors
20.02.1917	E.W. Petter	Control of fuel to engines
19.02.1918	E.W. Petter	Control of fuel to engines
19.02.1918	"	Internal combustion engines
18.02.1919	P.W. Petter	Motor plough and tractor
18.02.1919	Petters Ltd	Eye protection for welders
18.02.1919	"	Internal combustion engines
23.02.1920	"	Pneumatic motors for mechanical musical instruments
23.02.1920	"	Pneumatic musical instruments
23.02.1920	"	Tune-sheet winding mechanism
23.02.1920	"	Striking mechanism for musical instruments
23.02.1920	"	Internal combustion engines
23.02.1920	"	Liquid fuel burners
23.02.1920	"	Electric heating of engines before starting
1921		Auto-pianos
1922	E.W. Petter	Internal combustion engines
1922	G.B. Petter	" " "
1922	"	Joint-making packing
1922	"	Lubrication
1922	P.W. Petter	Gas engines
1922	"	Lubrication
1922	Petters Ltd	Gas engines
1922	"	Electric switches
1922	"	Lubrication
1923	G.B. Petter	Calculating machines
1923	Petters Ltd	Internal combustion engines
1925	E.W. Petter	" " "
1925	G.B. Petter	Calculating machines
1925	Petters Ltd	Aircraft
1926	"	Fuel pumps
1926	"	Resilient telescopic struts (undercarriage)
1927	E.W. Petter	Advertising devices
1927	Petters Ltd	Gun mountings
1929	"	Milking machines

1930	Petters Ltd	Manoeuvring trolleys
1930	"	Milking machines
1930	"	Internal combustion engines
1930	"	Starting internal combustion engines
1930	"	Pistons for internal combustion engines
1930–1931	"	Thermostatic control of electric starters
" "	"	Brakes for aircraft
" "	"	Aircraft
1931–1932	G.B. Petter	Calculating machines
" "	Petters Ltd	Calculating machines
" "	"	Metal spars for aircraft
" "	"	Aluminium magazines for aircraft
" "	"	Lubricators
1933–1934	Petters Ltd	Cockpit windshields
" "	"	Calculating machines
" "	"	Clips for securing cables
1936–1937	P.W. Petter	Internal combustion engines
" "	Petters Ltd	Wheel braking mechanism
" "	"	Internal combustion engines
1937–1938	W.E.W. Petter	Aircraft
" "	Petters Ltd	Starting diesel engines
1938–1939	"	Internal combustion engines
1940–1941	W.E.W. Petter	Retracting undercarriage for aircraft
" "	"	Cooling internal combustion engine exhaust
1941–1944	"	Remote-control apparatus
" "	"	Control surfaces for aircraft
1944–1946	"	Inflatable gaskets
" "	"	Pressure cabins for aircraft
" "	"	Engine mountings for aircraft
" "	"	Sliding roofs for aircraft
" "	"	Gun mountings for aircraft
1948–1949	"	Aircraft doors

W.E.W. Petter with English Electric Co. Ltd

1953–1954		Petter & Bradford aircraft air brakes
1954–1955		Jet-propelled aircraft
1957–1958	Petters Ltd	(Law) Compression ignition engines
1958–1959	W.E.W. Petter	Aircraft armaments
1959–1960	Petters Ltd	(Johns & Silberstein) Fuel-injection pumps

1962–1963	Petters Ltd	(Silberstein) Internal combustion engine nozzles
1962–1963	"	(Silberstein) Air filters
1965–1966	"	(Hawkes) Extracting oil from oil sump
1968	"	(Smith) Compression ignition engines
1968–1969	"	(Joseph) Starting handles for internal combustion engines
1968–1969	"	(Salmon) Internal combustion engines
1969	"	(Joseph & Knoyle) Controls for compression ignition engines
1970–1971	"	(Noble) Engine starters
1979	"	(Jacobs) Temperature control system

Index